Great Ghosts

*Also by Aidan Chambers
in Piccolo*

Haunted Houses
This Place is Haunted

Aidan Chambers

Great Ghosts

Piccolo Books

Originally published in two separate volumes in Piccolo

This Piccolo edition published 1991 by
Pan Books Ltd,
Cavaye Place, London SW10 9PG

1 3 5 7 9 8 6 4 2
Text © Aidan Chambers 1971, 1973, 1991

Illustrations © Pan Books Ltd 1991

Phototypeset by Intype, London

ISBN 0 330 31107 7

Printed in England by Clays Ltd, St Ives plc

Contents

The Ghost and the Pious Woman

Powis Castle in Monmouthshire stands high above the River Severn, a solid fortress made beautiful by some of the finest gardens in Britain, gardens which have remained almost unchanged in design since they were first cultivated two hundred and fifty years ago. The place is worth a visit, and anyone who goes there ought to know about its ghost.

In 1780, a poor old woman came to Powis looking for work. She made her living by spinning, going from farm to farm in the country round Welshpool, picking up work wherever she could, and staying a day or two with the farmer's family until the job was complete. The old woman was known to be very religious, entirely honest and trustworthy, so most of the farmers she called on tried their best to find something for her to do, whether they really wanted her services or not. One day when she arrived at Powis Castle (known then as Red Castle) the earl was away in London, but his steward, in charge during his master's absence, set the old woman to work.

By nightfall, as she was still busy, the steward's wife told the old woman she could stay till next day, and a room was prepared for her to sleep in. It was a ground floor room with a board floor and two sash windows, grandly furnished with a handsome bed in one corner. The servants had built a good fire to warm the place and in these sumptuous surroundings the old woman, used to a straw mattress in an attic rather than to such luxury, was left to herself for the night. Only when she was alone did she wonder at the steward providing for her so well. And when she came to think of it, she realized the servants who showed her into the room had seemed very keen to be gone as quickly as they could. They did not stop to gossip as servants usually did. Indeed, they had almost dashed out, closing the door firmly behind them. Still, the old woman was used to taking whatever came her way, and life was full of surprises. So she sat herself by the fire and, as was her nightly custom, settled herself to read a chapter of her Bible before going to bed.

She had not been reading for more than a few minutes when she heard her bedroom door open. Looking up, she was astonished to see a man enter the room, for this was no ordinary man, not one of the servants, but a gentleman, a man of wealth and authority. He wore a gold-laced hat, and his coat and waistcoat and everything else about him were of the finest quality. He walked across the room to the window in the corner and back again to the other window, the bottom of which was chest high. There he stood, half turned towards the old woman, his elbow on the window ledge and his face resting in the palm of his hand. He stayed like this for some time, during which the old woman stared at him, fascinated. She had never seen him before, and all the while she felt that he was waiting for her to speak. But so taken aback was she by his unexpected entry that she could not utter a word. After some while, the gentleman walked off, closing the door behind him.

Shock at the gentleman's arrival gave way now to terror, as the old woman realized that what she had seen was not a man of flesh and blood, but an apparition. The figure had been a ghost, and the servants had known it would appear. That was why they had put her in this grand bedroom, with its fine and comfortable bed. They knew about the ghost and wanted to see what would happen when it confronted a pious old woman. This is what she guessed – and she was right.

At once she threw herself on to her knees and began praying for help and protection. While she prayed the ghost returned, walked across the room and came close up behind her. Still kneeling, the old woman tried to speak but was so stricken with fear she could not utter a sound. The ghost turned and walked out of the room again, once more closing the door behind it.

Alone for a second time, the old woman managed to calm herself, making up her mind that if the ghost came back she would keep her wits about her and speak to it. Thus resolved, she sat down to await another visitation, her eyes keeping watch on the door.

Sure enough, after only a few moments the door swung open and the ghost entered, walked across the room, and came up behind her just as it had done on its second appearance. Turning her head to face the apparition, the old woman asked as firmly as she could, 'Pray, sir, who are you and what do you want?'

Raising its finger, the ghost replied, 'Take up the candle and follow me, and I will tell you.'

The woman obeyed and followed the ghost out of the room, a candle clutched in her trembling hand. She was led through a long passage till they reached the door of a room which the ghost opened and passed through. The room was small, hardly bigger than a cupboard. Feeling even more afraid, for she had no wish to be shut in so small a place with a ghost, the old woman stopped at the door. The ghost turned to her and said, 'Walk in. I will not hurt you.'

With the courage only the innocent and faithful possess, the old woman went inside.

'Observe what I do,' said the ghost then.

It stooped and lifted up one of the floorboards. Underneath was a box with an iron handle in the lid.

'Do you see that box?' asked the ghost.

'I do,' said the old woman.

The ghost stepped to one side of the room and showed the old woman a crevice in the wall, where it said a key was hidden which would open the box.

'This box and key,' it said, 'must be sent to the earl in London. Will you see it done?'

'I'll do my best,' said the old woman.

'Do, and I will trouble this house no more,' said the ghost, then walked out of the room and disappeared down the passage.

As soon as the old woman saw that the ghost had vanished, she went to the room door and shouted loudly. The steward and his wife and all the other servants ran to her at once; they had been waiting full of curiosity to see what would happen, and now they crowded round the old woman, frightened and full of questions.

The old woman told them all that had taken place and showed the box and key. The steward was afraid to meddle at all, but his wife was less timorous. With the help of some of the servants she hauled the box from its hiding place, took the key from the crevice and carried both off to prepare them for dispatch to the earl.

It would be satisfying to know what that heavy, iron-bound box contained, but the old woman, who told the story to Mr John Hampson, a Methodist preacher, never saw it opened and was never told by anyone what was found inside. All she did know was that on his return from London the earl took the old woman into his care, paying for whatever she wanted – which was never very much – and even offering her rooms of her own at the castle and any comforts she desired to go with them. The old woman, as modest as she was pious, made very few demands on the earl's gratitude. But we can only assume from the earl's behaviour that the box contained such treasure that nothing its finder could ask for in reward could possibly match it in value. As for the ghost, it kept its word as the old woman had kept hers. It has never been seen again.

The Haunting
of Hinton Ampner

Anyone who is interested in ghosts and the places they haunt will sooner or later come across the remarkable story of the twenty-year-long haunting of Hinton Ampner Manor House, which stood near Alresford in Hampshire. Even though the events took place two hundred years ago, the details remain convincing, because they were carefully recorded by a variety of eye-witnesses, and by one of the ghost's victims in particular, Mrs Mary Ricketts.

As we must rely on Mrs Ricketts for the best evidence, we should look at her closely. She was the daughter of Admiral Jervis, the seaman who fought and won the battle of Cape St Vincent, a victory for which he was rewarded by elevation to the peerage, taking the title Earl St Vincent. Other members of this talented family held high posts in church and government. Mrs Ricketts's husband was William Henry Ricketts, a rich lawyer who owned a great deal of land in the West Indies. Mary herself was held by everyone – relatives, friends, servants – in the deepest respect. She was, they all said, incapable of telling a lie. Her no-nonsense mind was as sharp as a needle and her will-power and courage impregnable. In fact, she seems to have been a formidable but kindly woman, and, as a witness in a case of ghostly activity, as reliable as anyone can be. This does not mean, however, that she was incapable of making a mistake, or that everything she recorded must be accepted without question. What it does mean is that we can trust that she set down her experiences as honestly and as sincerely as she could manage. The difficult thing is to decide accurately just what caused the events she describes, and whether her interpretations of them are the right ones.

The story begins in 1765 when the Ricketts rented the manor house. From the time they arrived they heard strange noises. Mrs Ricketts frequently went round the house looking for the cause but never found an explanation. Towards the end of 1769 Mr Ricketts sailed off to Jamaica to attend to his land, leaving his wife, three young children and eight servants at Hinton Ampner. He had not been gone long before the haunting became serious and frightening. Some of the servants left; before the ghost was done with them, all eight had fled and the ones who replaced them never stayed long.

Readers who want to study the various pieces of written evidence will find it in Sacheverell Sitwell's book *Poltergeists* (Faber and Faber) and in the *Journal of the Society for Psychical Research*, Vol. VI, April 1873. What I have done in the following pages is to take

Mrs Ricketts's own account and rewrite it in modern English, to remove the old-fashioned language and the repetitive passages. The facts are, of course, unchanged.

The Haunting of Hinton Ampner adapted from the account written by Mrs Mary Ricketts

About six months after we came here, Elizabeth Brelsford, who was nanny to our eight-month-old son Henry, was sitting by the baby as he slept in the room over the pantry, which we had made into a nursery. It was a hot summer's night so the nursery door had been left open. From where she was sitting, Elizabeth could look across the landing to the door of the yellow bedroom, the one usually occupied by the mistress of the house. As she sat there she saw quite clearly a gentleman dressed in a drab-coloured suit enter the yellow bedroom. She was not at all surprised at the time but when the housemaid, Molly Newman, brought up her supper, Elizabeth asked who the stranger was. When Molly replied that there was no stranger in the house, she described what she had seen. Together the two servants made a search of the bedroom. But they found no one. By this time, Elizabeth was very upset. She was absolutely certain about what she had seen and the light was good enough to distinguish any object clearly.

When I heard Elizabeth's story I dismissed it as

superstitious nonsense. I have had to change my opinion since.

In the autumn of the same year, 1765, George Turner, the son of the gardener at that time, while crossing the great hall on his way to bed, saw at the other end a man in a drab-coloured coat. He took him to be the butler, because a new one had just then arrived and had not yet had his livery made. But when George got upstairs to the menservants' dormitory he was astonished to find all of them, including the new butler, in bed. The man in the drab-coloured suit once again could not be accounted for.

In July 1767, at about seven one evening, four of the servants were sitting in the kitchen when they heard a woman coming downstairs, her dress rustling in the way the stiffest silk would. The servants turned to see who the woman might be and saw a tall figure wearing dark-coloured clothes rush past the kitchen door in the direction of the outside entrance to the house. At this moment, the cook was on her way into the kitchen. The figure passed close by her. Startled, the cook and the other servants discussed the incident; and their shocked surprise was heightened when a man coming from the yard into the house from the direction taken by the figure denied having met anyone at all.

Some time after my husband left for Jamaica late in 1769, I frequently heard, as I lay in bed, the noise of someone walking about in my dressing-room next door, and the rustle of silk clothes against the door leading to my bedroom. The noise was sometimes so loud and went on for so long that I could not sleep. Though I often searched the dressing-room as soon as the noises began, I never found anyone there.

After the disturbances had happened a number of times, I made it my practice to search the room and its cupboards and to lock the landing door into the dressing-room from the inside so I could be certain no one could get in without passing through my bedroom. Then I always fastened the door from the dressing-room into my bedroom with a draw-bolt on my side. Even these precautions did not prevent the disturbances, however. They went on uninterrupted.

I was lying awake in the yellow bedroom one night in the summer of 1770 when I heard the plodding tread of a man's footsteps coming towards the foot of my bed. I had been in bed about half an hour, wide awake and without any feelings of fear or apprehension. Now, as the footsteps approached, I thought the danger too close to ring the bell for assistance. Instead I sprang out of bed and ran from the room into the nursery opposite. Hannah Streeter, who had replaced Elizabeth as the children's nanny, was in the nursery and together we took a lamp and searched my room. But in vain.

This new disturbance upset me greatly, for the frightening noises were now in my own room, not away from me safe behind a locked door. Nevertheless, I plucked up courage and went back to bed without coming to any conclusion about the cause of the trouble.

For some months afterwards I heard nothing of any particular note until the November of the same year. I had by then moved to a warmer bedroom over the hall and lying there once or twice heard the sound of music and, on one night especially, heard three distinct knocks, as though made with a club or something heavy, against a door downstairs. It occurred to me that burglars might be trying to break in, but before I could summon help, the noise ceased and I thought nothing more of it for the time being. After this, early in 1771, I was frequently aware of a hollow murmuring noise that seemed to fill the whole house. It was not made by the wind, as you might expect, because I heard it on the calmest nights. Besides, I had never heard it before in all the five years of our living in the house.

On the morning of 27 February 1771 my maid, Elizabeth Godin, came into my room, and I enquired about the weather. She replied in such a faint voice that I asked if she were ill. No, she said, she was well, but had never in her life been so terrified as during the past night. She had heard the most evil groans, and fluttering noises round her bed for hours on end. She had got up and searched the room, even looking up the chimney, but though it was a bright, moonlit night, she could find nothing unusual. I said nothing

to Elizabeth but hoped she would not find out that
the room she slept in had formerly been occupied by
Mrs Parfait, the old housekeeper who had died a few
days before at Kilmston and had been buried in
Hinton churchyard on the evening of the night when
this disturbance happened. I knew if Elizabeth discovered this, she would refuse to sleep in the room.

That same day five weeks later, 2 April, I awoke
between one and two o'clock (I knew the time because
my watch was beside a rushlight on my bedside table.)
I lay wide awake for some minutes before I heard
people walking about in the passage outside, between
my room and the nursery. I got out of bed and listened
at the door for about twenty minutes, in which time
I distinctly heard the footsteps and also a loud noise
like someone pushing hard against a door. By now I
was convinced my senses were not playing tricks. So
I rang my bell for help, something I had not done at
once because I did not want to disturb Hannah Streeter, who was ill with a fever. My maid, Elizabeth
Godin, was having to look after Hannah and my three
sons too, in the nursery.

When Elizabeth came, I asked her if she had seen
anyone in the passage. No, she said, she had not. I
joined her outside my room. There was a window in
the passage which I examined in case someone had
gained entrance that way. It was shut tight. We
looked under a couch which stood in the passage, the
only furniture there that could conceal anyone. The

door into the passage was locked, as it ought to have been so that no one could enter our part of the house during the night.

Having thus searched thoroughly, I stood and pondered with much astonishment, when suddenly the door into the yellow room shook as if being rattled to and fro by someone standing behind it.

This was more than I could bear. I ran into the nursery and pulled the bell, which rang in the menservants' quarters. Robert Camis came to the passage door. I let him in, told him why I had summoned him, armed him with a stout stick of wood to use as a club, and waited while he opened the yellow room door.

No one was found. The room was in order and there was no way out.

I dismissed Robert, fastened the door, and went to bed in the nursery, not caring to be on my own again that night, and a little afraid also for Elizabeth. About half an hour later, I heard three clear knocks, just like those earlier. They seemed to come from somewhere below but I could not then or later discover the spot. Next night I slept in my own room and now and then heard noises and often the hollow murmur mentioned before.

On 7 May, exactly five weeks later, the murmur was unusually loud. I could not sleep because of it, all the time expecting something to happen. So I got up and went into the nursery where I stayed until half-past three, and then, when dawn was breaking, went back to my own room, hoping to get some sleep. It was not to be, however, for at ten minutes to four the great hall door directly below me was slammed to with such violence that my room shook from the force of it. I jumped out of bed and ran to the window that overlooked the porch. There was plenty of daylight now, but I saw nothing that could explain the noise. When the door was examined it was found securely locked and bolted as usual.

From this time on I had my maid Elizabeth Godin bring her bed and sleep in my room. The noises grew more frequent, and Elizabeth always heard the same sounds as I, and coming from much the same direction as I thought they did. By now, I was harassed and perplexed, but very unwilling to tell anyone else of my anxiety. I had taken every possible precaution in having the house thoroughly investigated but could discover no evidence whatever of trickery. On the contrary, I became convinced the disturbances were beyond the power of any living human being to perform. But knowing what effect my convictions would have on the rest of the household, I held my tongue.

After midsummer the noises grew worse every night. They began before I went to bed and continued without pause till daybreak. I could often make out voices – usually a shrill female voice to begin with, joined later by two others, deeper, more masculine in tone. But though this conversation seemed to be going on quite close to me, I could never distinguish the words.

Often I asked Elizabeth if she heard any noise. Always she answered by describing exactly what I had heard myself. One night in particular the curtains round my bed rustled as if something had brushed against them. I asked Elizabeth if she had seen anything. Her reply spoke my thoughts!

Several times I heard music – not regular notes or a tune, but a harmonious sound. Every night I heard walking, talking, knocking, the opening and banging closed of doors. My brother, Captain John Jervis, came to stay. But I could not bring myself to discuss these matters with him. They seemed so improbable, so fanciful when spoken of in the calm of day. The noises went on happening while he was with me, however, and I was naturally curious to know if he heard them too. So one morning I casually said, 'I was afraid last night the servants would disturb you, and rang my bell to order them to bed.'

My brother replied that he had heard nothing!

The night after he left me, at about three o'clock in the morning when daylight was already showing, Elizabeth and I both heard the most loud, deep, tremendous crash, as if some fast-moving object had fallen to the floor with extreme force just outside my room. We both started up in our beds, Elizabeth looking round her, expecting, as she always did, to see something terrifying.

'Good God!' I cried. 'Did you hear that noise?'

Elizabeth made no reply, so I repeated my question.

'I was that frightened,' she said at last in a faltering voice, 'I scarce dared to speak.'

At this very moment we heard a shrill, dreadful shriek, which seemed to come from under the spot where the falling object fell. The ghastly scream was repeated three or four times, each time fainter than before, as though it were descending slowly into the bowels of the earth.

Lying in the nursery, poor Hannah Streeter heard these noises too, and was so terrified that for two hours she was struck dumb and motionless. To this point, Hannah had heard little of the ghost, and what she had heard she dismissed without giving it much thought. But after this experience, instead of wanting to have no more to do with such strange events, the foolish girl was consumed with curiosity and said she would very much like to hear more of the sounds. Her rash wish was granted. From then until she left the house there was scarcely a night that her sleep was not broken by the sound of footsteps coming towards her door and someone pushing against it as though attempting to force it open.

I was so alarmed myself by this turn of events that I determined to tell my brother about all that was happening when next he visited us. Meanwhile, the constant interruption of my sleep affected my health; I developed a deep cough and a fever.

The morning after my brother at last arrived for his next visit, having warned him that I had something to tell him that would require all his trust in me to believe, I began my story. John listened, surprise and wonder showing on his face. Just as I finished, Captain Luttrell, a neighbour at Kilmston, happened to call, and John told him about the troubles. Together they decided to investigate. We agreed that Captain Luttrell should come to us late that evening, and that my brother and he should divide the night between them, one keeping watch while the other slept. This plan we told to no one else, for obvious reasons.

That evening my brother, accompanied by his man-servant, John Bolton, searched every room in the house, including the attics, looked into every possible hiding place, and made certain each door was locked after him, except those rooms occupied by the family. This done, he went to bed in the room above the servants' hall.

Captain Luttrell and John Bolton, armed with weapons, sat up in the room next to my brother's.

I slept that night in Elizabeth's room, while the children were in the nursery. Thus, every room on that floor was occupied.

As soon as I lay down I heard a rustling as of a person close to the door. I ordered Elizabeth to sit up for a while, and, if the noise continued, to go and tell Captain Luttrell.

Elizabeth heard the noise, and instantly Captain

Luttrell's room door was thrown open and we heard him speak.

The Captain told us next morning that he had heard the footsteps of someone walking across the passage. Instantly he threw open his door.

'Who goes there?' he demanded.

The 'something' flitted past him.

Just then my brother called out, 'Look against my door.'

He too had heard the noise, which seemed to him to be approaching his room. Getting up, he joined the Captain. Both were astonished and now heard various other noises. They looked everywhere but found nothing.

My brother and John Bolton went upstairs to the servants' rooms but found everyone in bed and all the doors secured as they had been earlier. Captain Luttrell and my brother then sat up till daybreak, when my brother returned to his own room.

About this time I heard the door of the Captain's room slam with great violence, and immediately afterwards a door downstairs slammed also. An hour later the main door into the house closed with such force that the building shook to its foundations.

At breakfast that morning I mentioned the doors banging, and was somewhat surprised to learn that Captain Luttrell had thought that it was my door and the one into the room next to mine that had made the row. Odder still, my brother had not heard the doors slamming at all but instead had listened to dreadful groans which he could not explain.

In discussing our restless night on watch, Captain Luttrell said that he believed the disturbances were of such a nature that the house ought not to be lived in. My brother agreed, and we decided to let the owners know what we thought.

Meanwhile, my brother sat up every night for the next week. In the middle of one of these nights I was startled by the noise of a gun going off between my room and the nursery, immediately followed by groaning, as of a person in agony or even dying. The strange thing was that no one else heard these things.

Several more inexplicable noises were heard by different members of the household during the next few days. But never did we discover their cause, and finally my brother returned to Portsmouth, from where he sent his captain of marines to help me pack up and leave Hinton Ampner.

One circumstance more is worth noting: the effect of these events on my favourite cat. She would be sitting quietly on a chair or table when suddenly she would slink down as if terrified, and dive under my chair and put her head close to my feet. A few moments later she would come out and behave calmly again. Never at these times did I see or hear anything that might have alarmed the animal, and I had never seen her act like this before the disturbances began, nor did I ever do so after we left that house. The servants told me that a spaniel dog that lived with them would now and then behave in just this curious manner.

Mrs Ricketts's account of this nerve-wracking haunting was written a year after the events described. Several theories have been put forward since then about the cause of the phenomena. Some people believe the noises were the work of restless, guilty spirits – those of Lord Stawell and his sister-in-law, Honoria, who are supposed to have had a love affair in secret when they lived in the house some years before the Ricketts arrived. A baby was born of this relationship, and it is said, was murdered to avoid anyone knowing what was going on. That wicked crime left its ghosts to haunt the house, as well it might.

A less horrifying explanation, however, may be quite simply as unspooky as this: about the time of the disturbances, heavy rainfall broke all records and this was followed by extreme frosts, snow, hail and winds. Such entirely natural, even if unusually harsh, conditions could very easily have affected the stability of the building, causing its old timbers to crack, its foundations to move, and what were in effect miniature earthquakes to take place in the ground on which the house stood. Such things have been known to create eerie noises and frightening movements inside buildings and people have thought they were being haunted by ghosts.

This is the trouble with hauntings. Even the most convincing of them may be nothing more than ordinary happenings which are misinterpreted by people who jump too easily to wrong conclusions. On the other hand . . . who knows *beyond doubt*? Whatever might have caused the troubles at Hinton Ampner, Mrs Ricketts believed till her dying day that she had been the victim of a ghost out haunting.

The Ghost
of Grandpa Bull

Samuel Bull, a chimney-sweep by trade, died in his cottage in Oxford Street, Ramsbury, Wiltshire, in June 1931. For four years he had been ill, nursed by his faithful wife, Mary Jane. But the strain of caring for her husband and her grief at his death finally took their toll. Soon after Samuel's funeral Mary Jane fell ill herself, took to her bed, and remained there, a bed-ridden invalid for the rest of her days.

Mary Jane's grandson, James Bull, tried to nurse the ailing woman and to keep house and earn a living at the same time. It was a makeshift arrangement that could not last for long. That August, Mrs Edwards, Grandma Bull's married daughter, moved into her mother's cottage, accompanied by her husband and five children, the eldest of which was a girl of fourteen.

The problem of how to look after Mary Jane was solved. But the solution brought new problems in its wake. Nine people were now packed into the little house in Oxford Street. To make matters worse, the building was badly in need of repair. Shortly after the Edwards family moved in some of the rooms had to be shut up because they were too damp to use. In these unhappy circumstances, Mrs Bull and her relatives spent the autumn and winter months.

It was during February 1932 that the haunting began.

No doubt as a result of the overcrowded, damp conditions in which they lived, one after another the children fell ill with flu, which in those days was still a dangerous sickness. To make them as comfortable as possible and to protect Grandma Bull from infection, three of the children who shared the old woman's bedroom were brought downstairs to the living-room. They had been there a fortnight when, one evening that February, they lay in the candlelight unable to sleep. They complained that someone was lurking outside. They were quite sure of it, even though neither they nor their mother, who was sitting with them, could hear anyone.

So persistent were the restless children that at last Mrs Edwards opened the door and looked around outside. No one was there; but if she hoped this would settle the children down, she was disappointed. Still they were uneasy – half excited, half fearful, as if expecting the arrival of a strange visitor. This, at least, is how they explained their feelings later, feelings they experienced every time the ghost appeared.

Their instincts had been right. A strange visitor was indeed on his way. Only a short while after Mrs Edwards had looked outside, she and the children were struck dumb when they saw the apparition of

Samuel Bull suddenly make itself visible. As they watched in wide-eyed shock, the figure walked up the stairs and entered the room in which the old man had died – one of those the family had recently shut up because of the dampness.

At that moment the children found their voices and screamed. No one can blame them for that. Their grandfather's ghost looked as solid as Samuel Bull had looked in his life, and it was dressed just as he had been when returning home from work each day. But the Edwards children knew very well that Samuel had been dead and buried for eight months past, and that what they saw, therefore, could be nothing other than a spectre.

We can imagine the flurry of nervous excitement that must have agitated the entire household during the rest of that haunted night, for everyone saw the apparition. However, when Grandma Bull heard news of this extraordinary event she was not a bit startled. She had seen the ghost before, she said. She and her family were to see it again, many times.

So frequently did the ghost visit the house, in fact, that the children grew accustomed to its arrival. For about half an hour before anyone could see it, its presence was felt. They all knew the spirit was with them, invisible but unmistakably *there*. Mrs Edwards said she felt at these times 'as though I was expecting my brother from America or something like that'. Then, quite suddenly, the ghost would become visible, as solid-looking and lifelike as any of those watching it.

Always the ghost behaved in the same way. Climbing the stairs, it walked soundlessly into Grandma Bull's room, where it would stand by her bed and lay a hand on the old woman's forehead. The hand, said Mrs Bull, felt firm but cold. And once – only once – she heard the ghost speak. It uttered one word, the name by which Samuel himself had always called his wife: 'Jane'.

These eerie visits were never short, and on at least one occasion lasted several hours. No wonder the family were upset and exhausted each time. They may have grown accustomed to seeing the ghost and lost their fear of it, but they never lost their sense of awe. During the time the ghost was in the house the children would sit unnaturally quiet and still. Nor was there any special hour when the ghost would appear. It was irregular, and might turn up at any time of the day or night. But, just like a living person, it could only be seen at night if a light was burning. Towards the end of the haunting, however, Mrs Edwards said that it began to grow 'lighter', as though it were shining, and then, she said, if the ghost had come in the night she was sure she would have been able to see it in the darkness without the aid of a lamp.

There might have been a reason for this change in the ghost's appearance. Throughout the haunting everyone felt that the ghost was sad. They were quite sure, in fact, that it was worried about Grandma Bull, and the conditions in which she and the family were forced to live. During the haunting news came that a better house had been found for them by the local council. At once the ghost lost its sadness and began to give off the glow Mrs Edwards noted, a glow that could be felt as well as seen by the onlookers and which made them in their turn feel happy. From the time they moved into their new home, the family was left undisturbed by Samuel's apparition.

Was the ghost really the spirit of the dead Samuel Bull returning anxiously to watch over his unhappy wife? Or was it an hallucination experienced by everyone who lived in the impoverished conditions of that overcrowded, leaky house? Or was the ghost just a figment of Grandma Bull's fevered imagination passed by telepathy to each member of the family? Stranger things than this have been known before and since.

Ghosts at War

In war, men, women and children die ugly, unnecessary deaths. So it is not surprising that many stories are told about ghosts being seen at battlefields, and about apparitions of people appearing before their horrified relatives and friends. During the First World War thousands of such visions were reported. Cases like this one, told by the sister of a soldier who was actually dying at about the time she saw his ghost:

I was awakened one night by three figures entering the bedroom; one in white between two soldiers in khaki. I drew my husband's attention to it, but he could not see anything and said: 'Now, it's just fancy; try and get to sleep.' I was just going over when they entered for the second time. I shall never forget it, for I knew there must be something coming concerning my much-loved brother. Three weeks later I had a letter from his officer saying my brother had been killed on the night of my vision.

Soldiers engaged in a battle have often seen apparitions. A non-commissioned officer recorded his experience at such a time:

I was with my battalion in the retreat from Mons on or about 28 August 1914. The weather was very hot and clear, and between eight and nine in the evening, I was standing with a party of nine other men on duty, and some distance on either side there were parties of ten on guard. Immediately behind us, half of my battalion was on the edge of a wood, resting. An officer suddenly came up to us in a state of great anxiety and asked if we had seen anything startling. He hurried away from my tent to the next party of ten. When he had got out of sight, I, who was in charge, ordered two men to go forward out of the way of the trees in order to find out what the officer meant.

The two men returned saying they could see no sign of any Germans; at that time we thought that the officer must be expecting a surprise attack.

Immediately afterwards, the officer came back and, taking me and some others a few yards away, told us to look at the sky.

I could see quite plainly, in mid-air, a strange light which seemed to be quite distinctly outlined and was not a reflection of the moon, nor were there any clouds in the neighbourhood.

The light became brighter and I could see quite distinctly three shapes, one in the centre having what looked like outspread wings, the other two were not so large, but were quite plainly distinct from the centre one.

They appeared to have a long, loose hanging garment of a golden tint and they were above the German line facing us.

We stood watching them for about three quarters of an hour. All the men with me saw them, and other men came up from the groups who also told us they had seen the same thing.

I remember the day, because it was a day of terrible anxiety for us. The Uhlans had attacked us and we drove them back with heavy loss. It was after this engagement, when we were dog-tired, that the vision appeared.

Other soldiers described this vision, too. One man claimed that the figures 'kept growing brighter and brighter. The faces could be described, but you couldn't see what they were like. Under the feet of the three figures was a bright star and when the figures disappeared, the star remained.'

What was it these soldiers saw? Were there in fact heavenly bodies floating about in the sky? Or were the men so exhausted after their devastating battle that their weary minds played tricks on them? No one can answer these questions for certain. But one thing is sure: the soldiers experienced *something*. Exactly what, and whether or not they were seeing ghosts or suffering from hallucinations, remains a mystery. We can only wonder at and puzzle over the extraordinary things witnessed during wartime. A lieutenant-colonel, for example, recorded this story:

On the night of 27 August 1914, I was riding along in the column with two other officers. We had been talking and doing our best to keep from falling asleep on our horses.

As we rode along, I became conscious of the fact that in the fields on both sides of the road, I could see a very large body of horsemen. These horsemen had the appearance of squadrons of cavalry and they seemed to be riding across the fields, going in the same direction as we were going and keeping level with us. The night was not very dark. I did not say a word about it at first but I watched them for twenty minutes. The two other officers had stopped talking. At last one of them asked me if I saw anything in the fields. I then told him what I had seen. The third officer confessed that he too had been watching these horsemen for the past twenty minutes.

So convinced were we that they were really cavalry, that at the next halt one of the officers took a party of men out to reconnoitre but found no one there.

The night then grew darker and we saw no more.

Of course, we were all dog-tired and over-taxed, but it is an extraordinary thing that the phenomenon should have been witnessed by so many different people.

So far, all these ghosts were ones people encountered while war was being fought. But there is another kind of war ghost. These are apparitions of people who took part in battles waged long ago. J. R. W. Coxhead told the story of one of these ghosts in his book *Devon Traditions and Folklore*:

On a fine, sunny afternoon in the year 1904 a party of small children, led by a schoolmistress, were going for a walk up Marlpit's Hill to the south of the little market town of Honiton. They had just passed the bend in the road by the beautiful fifteenth-century Church of St Michael, and were nearing the little thatched cottage which used to stand on a narrow strip of ground on the right-hand side of the road, when suddenly the children noticed a strange-looking man coming down the hill towards them.

The man was exceptionally tall, and very wild of aspect. He was wearing a black, broad-brimmed hat, and a long brown coat, and he was staring straight in front of him in rather a dazed kind of way. His queer, old-fashioned clothes were tattered and torn, and much bespattered with mud.

As he passed by, the children stared at him with their eyes filled with apprehension. The schoolmistress, noticing the children's frightened glances, said in a surprised voice, 'What on earth are you all looking at?'

One of the children whispered nervously, 'We are looking at that funny man.'

'What silly nonsense!' said the mistress. 'I can't see any funny man. There is nobody on the road except ourselves.'

The children were so insistent about the fact that they had seen the man, and were able to describe his dress and wild appearance so clearly that the schoolmistress mentioned the peculiar incident to Miss Barnett, the headmistress, when she returned to the school on Church Hill after the walk.

On further inquiries being made, it was discovered that a man who was living in the cottage in 1685 took part in Monmouth's Rebellion, and fought at the Battle of Sedgemoor. When the ill-fated Duke's army was defeated, the man managed to escape from the dreadful scene of carnage that followed, and, by hiding during the day in ditches and travelling furtively by night, he eventually succeeded in reaching his cottage on the slopes of Marlpit's Hill.

Just as his wife and children were running from the cottage to greet the exhausted fugitive, a party of troopers from the Royal army galloped up and cut him to pieces with their cavalry swords, in full view of his horror-stricken wife and family . . .

A man living not far from the village of Offwell, near Honiton, told the author of this book that his father saw the ghost in 1907. He was walking up Marlpit's Hill one night when the full moon was riding high in the sky. It was almost as light as day, and suddenly the apparition appeared in the road ahead of him. He was terribly frightened, but before the thing vanished he noticed that it was very tall and

wore a black wide-brimmed hat.

Two Scotsmen had an equally interesting experience, which was later written down by the son of one of them:

As you wish to have an account of the vision which my father and grandfather saw in the neighbourhood of this place [Inverary], I will endeavour to comply with your request. I have heard it, with all its circumstances, so often related by them both, when together, as well as by my father separately, since my grandfather's decease, that I am as fully convinced that they saw this vision, as if I had seen it myself.

This vision was seen by them about three o'clock in the afternoon of a very warm, clear sunshiny day in the month of June or July, between the years 1746 and 1753. I cannot go nearer to ascertain the year. My grandfather was then a farmer in Glenary (which is within four miles of this place), and my father, who was at that time a young unmarried man, resided in the family with him.

On the morning of the day above-mentioned, my grandfather, having some business in Glenshiray, took my father along with him. They went there by crossing the hill which separates it from Glenary; and their business in Glenshiray having been finished a little after midday, they came round by Inverary, in order to return home.

As soon as they came to Gairan Bridge, and had turned towards Inverary, they were very much surprised to behold a great number of men under arms marching on foot towards them.

They stood a considerable time to observe this extraordinary sight, then walked slowly on, but stopped now and then, with their eyes constantly fixed on the objects before them. Meantime, the army continuing regularly to advance, they counted that it had fifteen or sixteen pairs of colours; and they observed that the men nearest to them were marching upon the road, six or seven abreast, or in each line, attended by a number of women and children, both below and above the road, some of whom were carrying tin cans and other implements of cookery, which, I am told, is customary on the march. They were clothed in red (but as to that particular circumstance I do not recollect whether my grandfather mentioned it or not, though I know my father did), and the sun shone so bright that the gleam of their arms, which consisted of muskets and bayonets, sometimes dazzled their sight. They also observed an animal resembling a deer or a horse, in the middle of a crowd of soldiers, who were, as they conjectured, stabbing and pushing it forward with their bayonets.

My father, who had never seen an army before, naturally put a number of questions to my grandfather (who had served in the Argyll Highlanders in assisting to suppress the rebellion of 1745) concerning the probable route and destination of the army which was now advancing towards them, and of the number of men it seemed to consist of. My grandfather replied that he supposed it had come from Ireland, and had landed at Kyntyre, and that it was proceeding to England; and that, in his opinion, it was more numerous than the army on both sides at the battle of Culloden. My father having particularly remarked that the rear ranks were continually coming forward in order to overtake those who were before them, and inquiring the reason, my grandfather told him that this was always the case with the rear; that the least obstacle stopped and threw them behind, which necessarily, and in a still greater degree, retarded the march of those who were behind them, and obliged them to come forward until they recovered their own places again. And he therefore advised my father, if he went into the army, to endeavour, if possible, to get into the front rank, which always marched with leisure and ease, while those in the rear were generally kept running in the manner he had seen.

My father and grandfather were now come to the Thorn Bush between the Gairan Bridge and the gate of the Deer Park, and at the same time the rear of the army had advanced very near the gate. And as the road forms a right angle at that gate, and the front of the army was then directly opposite them, they had, of course, a better opportunity of observing it minutely. The vanguard, they then observed, consisted of a party of forty or fifty men, preceded by an officer on foot. At a little distance behind them another officer appeared, riding upon a grey dragoon-horse. He was the only person they observed on horse-back, and from his appearance and station in the march they considered him as the commander-in-chief. He had on a gold-laced hat, and a blue hussar-cloak, with wide, open, loose sleeves, all lined with red. He also wore boots and spurs; the rest of his dress they could not see. My father took such particular notice of him, that he often declared he would know him perfectly well if he ever saw him again. Behind this officer the rear of the army marched all in one body, so far as they observed, but attended by women and children, as I mentioned above.

My father's curiosity being now sufficiently gratified, he represented to my grandfather that these men, who were advancing towards them, would force them to go along with them, or use them otherwise ill; and he therefore proposed that they should both go out of their way by climbing over a stone dyke which fences the Deer Park from the high road. To this my grandfather objected, saying that as he was a middle-aged man, and had seen some service, he believed they would not give any trouble to him, but at the same time he told my father that as he was a young man, and they might possibly take him along with them, he might go out of the way or not, as he thought fit. Upon this my father instantly leaped over the dyke.

He then walked behind it for a little time; but when he arrived near the clumps, he looked back to observe the motions of the army, and found, to his utter astonishment, that they were all vanished, not a soul of them was to be seen.

As soon as he had recovered from his surprise, he returned to my grandfather, and cried out, 'What has become of the men?' My grandfather, who did not seem to have paid them much attention after my father left him, then observed also that they had disappeared, and answered back with an equal degree of astonishment, 'that he could not tell'.

As they proceeded on their way to Inverary, he recommended my father to keep what he had seen secret, lest they should make themselves ridiculous, for that no person would believe they had seen a vision so extraordinary; at the same time he told him that though he (my grandfather) might not live to see it, my father might possibly live to see the vision realized.

This conversation was scarcely ended, when they met one Stewart, an old man who then resided in Glenshiray, going home, and driving a horse before him. This, as they believed, was the same animal they had before observed surrounded by a crowd. My father asked Stewart what had become of the people who were travelling with him. Stewart, not understanding the drift of the question, answered that nobody had been in company with him since he left Inverary, but that he never travelled in so warm a day, that the air was so close and sultry that he was scarcely able to breathe, and that his horse had become so weak and feeble that he was obliged to alight and drive it before him.

The account of this vision was communicated by my father and grandfather, not only to me, but to many others in this place and neighbourhood, it being scarcely possible that so extraordinary an occurrence could long be concealed. It is no doubt extremely difficult to account for it, but no person acquainted with my father or grandfather ever supposed that either of them was capable of inventing such a story; and accordingly, as far as I can understand, no person to whom they told it ever doubted that they told the truth. My grandfather died several years ago; my father died within these two years; but neither of them saw their vision realized.

The Haunted
Bowling Alley

Mr W. V. Cleveley wrote to me in 1973 about a strange experience he had had. His account is so interesting that I include it here just as he told it.

I am thirty-one years of age and having left school at fifteen I joined Rank Organization cinemas, and after six years, joined their Bowling Division. I was employed as a mechanic at the new Bowl in Brook Street in Chester. Before being a bowling centre the building had been the Gaumont Cinema.

When I started work there my boss was Mr Fred Dickenson, who had been chief projectionist at the Gaumont. We were talking together one day and I was told by Mr Dickenson about the resident ghost, whose name was George.

I have an open mind about such matters and I must admit I took what he told me with a large pinch of salt. He said that during the war he heard a noise on the projection box roof. There was one loud thud followed by two small thuds. At the time an air raid was in progress and Mr Dickenson and his assistant thought a German pilot had baled out and landed on the roof. The thuds sounded like a body dropping followed immediately by the legs hitting the roof. The roof was searched but nothing was found. This happened many times again, always during an air raid, and always nothing was found.

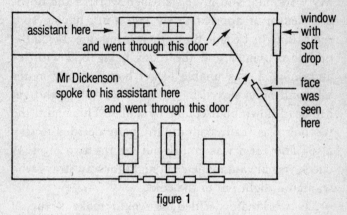

figure 1

Again in the same projection box there were three rooms (see drawing, figure 1). Mr Dickenson was running the show, in the main box; his assistant was in the rewinding room, spooling film. Mr Dickenson turned from the projector and looked towards a small window. In this window he saw the face of a man looking at him. He assured me that it was not his reflection in the glass nor light from the projector playing tricks. Mr Dickenson moved into the room his assistant was in and told him that somebody was in the other small room and to go through his door into the same room. It was impossible for anyone to be in the room and get out without passing either man; the only window opened to a drop of some eighty feet. When the two men entered the room it was empty.

Now, about my own experience of the same 'ghost'. My workmate and myself finished work at the Bowling Centre at approximately two a.m., having seen the Midnight League finish their last game. Being the middle of winter and the roads being bad with ice and snow, I was unable to get home on my motor bike and often stayed in the Bowl workshop and got my head down on a couple of chairs. This night, the weather was really bad and my mate decided to stay also. The Bowl was empty but for the two of us. A check was always made each night for any strays who wanted a night out of the cold.

My workmate decided he would make a cup of coffee before turning in; meanwhile I had a wash. My mate was in the workshop and I was having my wash in the staff room, approximately fifteen yards from the workshop (see drawing, fig. 2). There was a crash, and I thought, 'There go the cups.' Ready to go up in the air with my mate, I ran on to the old stage of the cinema, which after redevelopment had been left as no use could be made of it. On the stage I met my workmate who was on his way to see what I had dropped. We laughed and said it must have been George, and went back to what we had left. Within seconds of getting back to the washroom, I heard

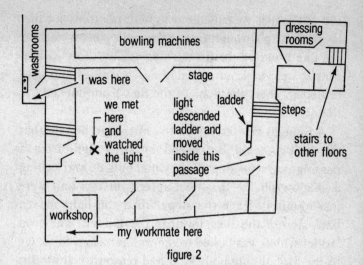

figure 2

another crash coming from the direction of the stage. I arrived back on the stage to meet my friend coming from the workshop. He had heard the second crash and came to look at what had happened. As the stage was not in use any more the only lights were four sixty-watt lamps, just enough light to see your way across to the bowling machines. In the centre of the stage we found a sheet of broken glass. On seeing this we thought it had fallen from the windows in the scenery flies which were almost one hundred feet above us. We looked up and in between the strips of wood that the men working on the scenery walked on, we could see something or someone moving across the flies. Thinking that someone might have broken in and managed to climb the single iron ladder to the top of the flies we called out to him, pointing out that he could slip through one of the pulley holes and fall the one hundred feet to the stage. The 'thing', whatever it was, took no notice of our warnings and continued to cross the floor of the flies from one side to the other.

A thought crossed my mate's mind and he said that the 'thing' could be caused by stray light from a passing car, reflecting off the canal outside and casting a shadow on the flies. We agreed on this and were just about to leave the stage when the light moved back across the flies towards the ladder. The iron ladder which was bolted to the wall ran from the stage to the top and anybody who had reason to climb this vertical ladder had a good climb in front of them. The light started to move slowly down the rungs of the ladder just as if someone was shining a torch on the ladder, and at this moment we realized that the light did not come from a car's headlights. It would be impossible for the reflection to shine at such an angle. Having reached the stage, the light passed through an open door and into a passage, and out of sight.

What we did next I cannot explain. My mate and myself telephoned the police and within minutes a number of policemen from Chester station of the Cheshire Police had positioned themselves around the whole building. My workmate and myself were confronted by an inspector and a sergeant. When we had finished, the inspector told the sergeant to climb the ladder to the top and see if he could find anything. I don't know if the sergeant was afraid of heights or what, but he refused to climb the ladder. At this, the inspector radioed for a dog and handler, and they arrived and were told our story.

The inspector asked us to show him where the passage led that the light went into. This was also part of the old cinema and led to the dressing-rooms in which the stars used to prepare themselves. These were no longer in use, and but for a few boxes, the rooms were empty.

Having passed through the passage we entered the small building by the only unlocked door. There were three rooms on the ground floor, three on the first floor, and one room built in the attic. As these rooms were not in use, there were no lights, so the police torches were the only illumination. The inspector told the dog handler to go in first with his dog. This he did with us all following behind. The dog led the way and sniffed around in all the rooms on the ground floor and first floor. But when he came to the attic he refused to pass through the door and even though the handler pulled on the lead the dog cried and cowered away, the fur on his back standing on end. The inspector rushed into the small room followed by the sergeant but it was completely empty. The dog still refused to enter, however. Later the handler said he had not seen anything like it before.

That was the last time I saw anything in the Bowl

even though I stayed there for another year.

This is the story as best I can remember it. I'm sure that a report was made to the Police HQ at Chester regarding that night. It happened in the winter of 1964.

The building is still standing, but is now a bingo hall. The stage is there but the dressing-rooms have been knocked down for a road to pass near the building.

As I said at the beginning, I keep a very open mind, but this sticks in my memory and even nine years later I still wonder what it was that happened that night.

The Ghost in Jail

One windy September night in 1835, Dr Henry Kerner, medical officer of Weinsberg jail, Germany, sat in a locked cell with a thirty-eight-year-old prisoner, Mrs Elizabeth Eslinger. At eleven-thirty the doctor heard a noise 'as of some hard body being thrown down on the side of the cell where the woman sat; she immediately began to breathe more rapidly . . . ' At that moment Mrs Eslinger broke the silence which had lasted for almost two hours. The ghost, she told the doctor, was present in the cell.

Dr Kerner placed a hand on the woman's forehead and commanded the evil spirit – for so he believed the ghost must be – to depart. According to his detailed report, the doctor then heard 'a strange rattling, cracking noise all round the walls which finally seemed to go out through the window. The woman said the spectre had departed.'

Mrs Eslinger had been troubled for many nights before this by an apparition which, she claimed, visited her in her cell. Dr Kerner had tried various treatments to cure his patient of what he considered at first to be a delusion, but had been forced against his better judgement to have himself locked in the woman's cell to see for himself what really did go on there. The inexplicable noises were no doubt a surprise to him, and his attempt to exorcize the ghost by commanding it to leave was perhaps the desperate remedy of a frightened man.

If he thought this extreme measure had succeeded where medicine had failed, he was soon proved wrong. To begin with, Dr Kerner had been sceptical. His experience in the cell forced him to think again. Something strange was certainly afoot; he was curious to know more, and he began investigating in earnest.

Ghosts, it turned out, were no strangers to Mrs Eslinger. She was, she said, a 'ghost seer'. Until the appearance of the prison apparition, though, she had never received messages. The Weinsberg ghost, however, was very communicative. It was upset, it said, that Dr Kerner had called it evil; it was nothing of the kind. Rather, it deserved and looked for pity, and requested Mrs Eslinger to pray nightly for its repose. It was, it claimed, the restless spirit of a Roman Catholic priest who had lived in Wimmenthal, Germany, in 1414. During his life the priest had committed a number of crimes, the worst of which was that he and his father had robbed his own brothers. Since his death his spirit had haunted the world, ever in despair, making its presence known to the living by moans and groans and an earthy but unusual smell. To Mrs Eslinger, its form was visible, and though she could not actually touch it, she said that when she reached out towards it she could feel its icy fingers in her hand, and that after a while they seemed to grow warmer.

Dr Kerner's first exorcism proved ineffective, and so another sitting was arranged on the night of 18 October. A similar scene took place. This time, however, a third person was present to witness the manifestations: Dr Kerner's wife. Again there was the noise of a heavy body being thrown down at Mrs Eslinger's side; again the doctor – more sympathetic this time – requested the spirit to leave his patient in peace. Again a rattling, cracking noise ran down the cell walls and disappeared, not through the window this time, but down the passage outside the cell.

Was it possible that the doctor was being tricked? Mrs Eslinger had been put into a thickly walled cell block which everyone considered completely secure and well-guarded. During the doctor's visits, the cell door was locked by the warder and all the other prisoners (many of whom also claimed to have seen the ghost) were carefully secured in their own cells. In such circumstances the authorities considered it extremely unlikely, perhaps even impossible, for anyone to produce night after night the peculiar effects heard and seen in Mrs Eslinger's cell without being caught in the act at some point.

By now, interest in the Weinsberg spectre had spread outside those impregnable prison walls. On 20

October, Justice Heyd accompanied Dr Kerner during yet another all-night vigil. Heyd cannot have been too convinced about the excitements to come (or maybe he had dined too well beforehand) for he kept nodding off to sleep. But the doctor, whose curiosity was intense, stayed wide awake.

The doctor's patience was rewarded. About midnight he witnessed an extraordinary sight. A small, shapeless cloud of yellowish light floated in through the glass of the narrow, barred cell window. It brought with it a cold breeze and a strong, earthy smell.

Justice Heyd, jerked out of his doze, was shocked by the eerie vision his sleepy eyes beheld. Kerner felt as if ants were running all over his face. Mrs Eslinger flung herself to her knees at her bedside and began praying with passionate fervour.

The two men watched the light as it floated up and down. While they did so, they heard a hollow, unearthly moan echoing round the room.

Two months later, on 9 December, Dr Kerner again saw this ethereal light, which, he said, looked 'like a little animal'. This time he was accompanied by Mrs Mayer, wife of the prison's deputy warden. Both heard a noise at the window so loud that they were sure the glass would shatter. Mrs Eslinger announced that the ghost had entered the room and was sitting on a stool.

Footsteps were then heard, as if someone was pacing up and down, and the cold breeze was felt again. And this time, both Dr Kerner and Mrs Mayer heard the same hollow, inhuman voice that had previously done no more than moan, uttering the words, 'In the name of Jesus, look on me!' At that moment the yellow light seemed to settle round them like a cloud, the footsteps sounded once more, and the voice said, 'Do you see me now?' And at last Dr Kerner did. The apparition stood in front of the window, a ghostly figure dressed in the clothes of a medieval priest.

Several times more during that eventful night the doctor saw the spectre, usually at Mrs Eslinger's side as she prayed. Finally, it came towards Mrs Mayer. She must have been a strong-minded woman for she confronted the approaching figure without flinching, and in a clear voice ordered, 'Go to my husband in his room and leave a sign that you have done so.'

'I will,' replied the unearthly voice.

The cell door was firmly locked, as always, but now it swung open, the apparition floated into the passage outside, and the heavy door closed again. Footsteps echoed through the cell block in the silence of the night.

A few moments later the ghost materialized again, standing by Mrs Eslinger's window. Had it done as it had been bidden, the curious investigators wanted to know. For answer, a hollow laugh filled the room.

Next morning, before his wife or Dr Kerner had mentioned anything about their adventures of the night before, Mr Mayer complained that his room

door had been standing wide open when he woke, and that he was certain he had locked and bolted it when he went to bed.

Dr Kerner felt he now had enough evidence and supporting witnesses to write a report. He described in it, as straightforwardly as he could, the facts as he had observed them, concluding with commendable restraint and scientific objectivity that whatever had been going on in Mrs Eslinger's cell it was certainly unusual and, to the best of his knowledge, could not be explained by the accepted laws of nature.

The published report excited widespread interest among scientists as well as the ordinary public. A stream of expert investigators visited Weinsberg. Well over fifty interviewed Mrs Eslinger and many of them were treated by the ghost to at least one of its party tricks: the rattling of bars in the window (which later proved to be solidly embedded and quite immovable), the hollow voice, the yellow light. Some of these people attempted to reproduce the effects. But try as they might none of them could achieve results that even vaguely resembled the hauntings. Two men heard a noise like gravel falling to the ground as they waited to see Mrs Eslinger. On being admitted to her cell they asked the ghost to repeat the noise, which it did. Two physicists, Dr Fraas and Dr Sicherer, said they saw a dense cloud suspended to one side of Mrs Eslinger's head, and during the night of their visit heard a thudding noise and saw the cell door open and slam shut eight separate times.

The idea that Mrs Eslinger herself might have caused the phenomena must have entered many people's heads, and ought to be considered. One occurrence seems to exonerate her from suspicion. Before she was released, the ghost promised to haunt the cell after she had gone. And it did. Two days after Mrs Eslinger's sentence ended, Mrs Mayer was witness to a number of sounds, none of which had been heard before.

According to Mrs Eslinger, the ghost had frequently pleaded with her to go to Wimmenthal after her release, there to pray for the peace of its soul. This she did, in the presence of many onlookers, who testified that, as she prayed, the figure of a man accompanied by two other smaller apparitions appeared before her. As she finished her prayer, Mrs Eslinger fainted. On reviving, she told how the ghost had asked for her hand. Before holding it out, she had taken care to wrap it in a handkerchief. The ghost touched her hand, and when it did so a flame flashed between them. As proof of this, the strangest event of this unusual haunting, Mrs Eslinger offered the protective handkerchief on which finger marks were clearly scorched.

For over a year between 1835 and 1836 the Weinsberg ghost appeared to the imprisoned Elizabeth Eslinger, but despite Dr Kerner's detailed and honest report, the testimony of scores of other witnesses, and the careful study experts have given the case over the years since it all happened, no one, even now, can say with any certainty just what caused the fascinating phenomena that kept people watching night after night in a cold prison cell. If we are to accept what Mrs Eslinger herself believed, then the ghost was indeed, as it claimed to be, the restless spirit of a sinful priest, a spirit that found at last a sympathetic mortal willing to help it find eternal peace.

Vampires

(Not to be read by the squeamish)

'VAMPIRE,' says Webster's *International Dictionary*, 'A blood-sucking ghost or reanimated body of a dead person believed to come from the grave and wander about by night sucking the blood of persons asleep, causing their death'. Belief in vampires, the most ghoulish of all ghosts, is hundreds of years old and can be discovered among people all over the world, though most popularly in Eastern Europe and least often in Britain and North America.

Details of the belief vary from place to place but the basic idea is generally the same. Vampires are thought to be the souls of dead witches, or of people who have committed suicide, or of anyone whose corpse was jumped over by an animal (a cat especially) or flown over by a bird. An evil spirit inhabits the dead body, which then rises from its grave and keeps itself 'alive' by feeding on the blood of living people while they lie asleep. Having had their blood sucked by a vampire, these unfortunate victims slowly fall ill, and eventually, after some days or even weeks of decline, they die, becoming vampires in their turn. So a vampire is a contradiction in terms: a living, dead body.

Catching a vampire and laying it to rest is a gruesome, not to say difficult, business. Because you cannot always distinguish an active vampire from an ordinary living person, you have to track it back to its grave. There you can easily see it is genuine because the body will look healthy and well-fed when it ought to be decomposed and wasted away. Putting an end to the monster is achieved, generally speaking, by one of two methods. A sharp stake must be driven through the vampire's corpse, particularly through the heart, pinning the body to the ground. Or the corpse must be burned until its flesh and bones are reduced to ashes.

There are more picturesque methods used in some places, however, such as the one recommended in Bulgaria.

Bulgaria's Bottled Vampire

Bulgaria, according to legend, abounds with vampires, and an ingenious trap has been devised to waylay them. You bottle them. A sorcerer, or ghost-catcher, arms himself with a holy charm – a picture of a saint, usually – and waits in ambush until the vampire passes by, when the sorcerer chases it, holding the charm in front of him. (Vampires cannot abide holy charms, apparently.) At once the monster will try to escape, seeking refuge from the sacred object. Eventually the ghost-catcher drives it up a tree or on

to the roof of a house where beforehand he has left
a specially prepared bottle in which is some of the
vampire's favourite food – human blood. Seeing the
irresistible food in the bottle, and anxious to escape
the pursuing sorcerer, the vampire makes itself small
by whatever supernatural power vampires and ghosts
in general possess, and enters the bottle. The sorcerer
has only to push a cork into the bottle for the vampire
to be trapped. Bottle and vampire are then thrown

into a fire and the vampire is thus destroyed for ever. (Why the vampire does not escape from the trap by putting to work for this purpose the same magic as it used to make itself small enough to get into the bottle has never been satisfactorily explained!)

Rather more seriously, though, we do know as a matter of historical fact that, about 1863, the inhabitants of a small village in Bulgaria were so afraid of what they believed to be an attack by many vampires that they shut themselves up in two or three houses, kept watch all night through, eventually called in an old woman reputed to be a witch, and asked her to rid them of the evil spirits. She did, but only after a night of horror in which howlings and shriekings and dire curses terrified the villagers. Blood was found next day sprinkled inside and outside the abandoned houses, and furniture had been hurled topsy-turvy in all directions. Whether this was really the work of vampires or was perhaps an extreme case of poltergeist activity, or simply an attack by thieves is now impossible to discover. What the incident shows, however, is that in Bulgaria at that time belief in vampires was so strong that such an event could be seriously blamed on them without anyone suggesting any other cause.

China and the head of Liu

Belief in vampires has been as strong in China as in Bulgaria, and there yet another means of catching them has been devised. You wait by the coffin until the corpse-spectre has left to go about its grisly business. You then scatter rice and peas and bits of iron round about, completely encircling its resting place. On returning, the vampire will not pass over this barrier of strange charms and you can capture it easily and burn it.

China also offers stories as gory as those to be found anywhere else, stories like the one about a teacher called Liu.

One summer Liu was given a holiday to tend his family grave, an important duty to the ancestor-worshipping Chinese of the times before the recent revolution. His duty done, his holiday over, Liu warned his wife that he must leave home early next day and so she rose at cock-crow and set about preparing her husband's breakfast. When the meal was ready, she went to Liu's room to wake him, but when she drew aside the curtains round his bed she found her husband lying across the bed, headless, and not a drop of blood anywhere. Terror-stricken, the poor woman ran to her neighbours crying for help, and they sent for the local magistrate.

The magistrate could find no culprit, and so, needing to show some results, he arrested Liu's wife. Who else, he argued, could have done it? He had no real evidence to prove this, but until he had, he locked the poor woman in jail for safe keeping. And there she languished for many months. She might have remained till death itself released her, had not a neighbour been passing a neglected grave one day and noticed that the tomb had been disturbed and the lid of the coffin was raised a little. His first thought was that thieves had broken in, hoping to rob the body of any jewels or valuables buried with it. So he called some friends and together they looked inside the coffin, intending to check that all was well before securing the tomb.

The sight they uncovered made them gasp. A corpse lay stretched in the coffin, its features as fresh and healthy as a living person's, its body covered with white hair. Between its arms was clutched the head of a man – a man they recognized only too readily: the head was Liu's. Again, the magistrate was brought. He ordered Liu's head to be removed from the arms of the vampire's corpse. The men tried to do as they were told, but their combined efforts could not budge it. At last the magistrate ordered that the arms should be cut off so as to release the head from their grasp. As this was done fresh blood gushed from the wounds. Afterwards, the body was burned, Liu's head decently buried, and his unjustly imprisoned and sorrowing widow set free.

Hungary's vampires galore

As recently as 15 February 1912,
the *Daily Telegraph* reported:

A boy of fourteen died some days ago in a small
[Hungarian] village. A farmer, in whose
employment the boy had been, thought that the
ghost of the latter appeared to him every night. In
order to put a stop to these supposed visitations, the
farmer, accompanied by some friends, went to the
cemetery one night, stuffed three pieces of garlic and
three stones in the mouth, and thrust a stake
through the corpse, fixing it to the ground. This was
to deliver themselves from the evil spirit.

By 1912, though belief in vampires was clearly still
strong among ordinary people in Hungary, the
authorities were less convinced. The farmer and his
friends were arrested for illegally tampering with a
grave. In earlier years the farmer's action would have
been entirely approved of, even considered cour-
ageous, a defence of his community against the
scourge of a vampire.

Iraq and the sad tale of Abul
and his beautiful bride

An old tale from Arabia as told by Fornari
in his *History of Sorcerers*:

In the beginning of the fifteenth century there lived

at Baghdad an aged merchant who had grown wealthy in his business and who had an only son to whom he was tenderly attached. He resolved to marry him to the daughter of another merchant, a girl of considerable fortune, but without any personal attractions. Abul-Hassain, the merchant's son, on being shown the portrait of the lady, requested his father to delay the marriage till he could reconcile his mind to it. Instead of doing this, however, he fell in love with another girl, the daughter of a sage, and he gave his father no peace till he consented to the marriage. The old man stood out as long as he could, but finding that his son was bent on acquiring the hand of the fair Nadilla, and was equally resolute not to accept the rich and ugly lady, he acquiesced.

The wedding took place with great pomp and ceremony, and a happy honeymoon ensued, which might have been happier but for one little circumstance which led to very serious consequences.

Abul-Hassain noticed that his bride quitted the nuptial couch as soon as she thought her husband was asleep, and did not return to it till an hour before dawn.

One night, filled with curiosity, Hassain, feigning sleep, saw his wife rise and leave the room. He rose, followed cautiously, and saw her enter the cemetery. By the straggling moonbeams he saw her go into a tomb: he stepped in after her.

The scene within was horrible. A party of ghouls

were assembled with the spoils of the graves they had violated and were feasting on the flesh of the long-buried corpses. His own wife, who, by the way, never touched supper at home, played no inconsiderable part in the hideous banquet.

As soon as he could safely escape Abul-Hassain stole back to his bed.

He said nothing to his bride till next evening when supper was laid, and she declined to eat; then he insisted on her partaking, and when she positively refused he exclaimed roughly, 'Oh yes, you keep your appetite for your feasts with the ghouls.' Nadilla was silent; she turned pale and trembled, and without a word sought her bed. At midnight she rose, fell on her husband with her nails and teeth, tore his throat, and, having opened a vein, attempted to suck his blood. He fled from her and on the morrow he opened the tomb, burnt her to ashes and cast the ashes into the Tigris.

The Stone-Throwing Ghost

At seven o'clock in the morning of Monday 21 September 1937, a stone fell on the roof of a bungalow in the rue Touraine, a street in Port Louis, capital of the crowded sub-tropical island of Mauritius. The stone bounced off the roof onto the paved courtyard below, frightening an eleven-year-old servant girl who fled at once into the house for safety. During the rest of this eventful day another forty or so stones were to rain on to the roof and into the courtyard. More surprising, and certainly more frightening for the occupants, at least that number fell *inside* the house and no one could tell where they came from.

Not unnaturally, the owner of the bungalow, Mr Cappy Ricks, supposed the stones were being thrown by mischievous boys. The police were called and a sharp look-out was kept all day long, without any success. No one was seen behaving suspiciously. The day's bombardment reached a climax that evening when a stone fell vertically into one of the bedrooms, while outside a shower of missiles poured into the courtyard. This final assault proved too much for the nerve-wracked servant girl. She rushed, shrieking, indoors and flung herself headlong under the dining-room table from where she was rescued in a state of collapse and sent home.

Next day, just after seven in the morning, the assault began again. This time more stones than ever fell, and mixed in among the stones were other objects, too. One in particular caught Mr Rick's eye. About seven inches long, wedge shaped, with a round hole near its thinner edge, it was to become very familiar before the disturbance ended, appearing here and there all over the house. Another was a large iron shackle minus its holding pin (the kind of tool used to link pieces of chain). It had been lying inoffensively in the courtyard for months, yet now it was flying dangerously about without apparent cause.

Again the police were summoned. At least two stood guard inside the house all day, while outside a third found himself a perch high up in a tree from where he had a bird's eye view of the bungalow, its grounds and the surrounding areas. His watch was fruitless. By the time night came and the barrage ended no one had been apprehended yet scores of stones had fallen, many inside the building even though all doors and windows were firmly closed.

The next day, Wednesday, the activity grew worse. In his own account, first published in *The Forum* of Johannesburg, Mr Ricks set down the details of this appalling experience:

While the cook was preparing breakfast, a large steel nut, that also had lain in the court during the whole of my tenancy, apparently fell from the low roof of the kitchen (the door and window being closed), and dashed a dish to pieces from her hands.

In an outside bathroom I was struck on the shoulder by a six-and-a-half-pound stone that had risen from the ground six feet away and entered the small room by a six-inch space above the door that gave it light. The inspector, who at that moment was leaning against a tree about six feet distant, had seen nothing. Only a thick bath towel saved me from injury.

Of the last four stones that fell this morning, one fell on a thin china plate on the dining table without even cracking it, although it had been observed to fall with something of a crash. Another fell between the necks of three bottles standing together on the sideboard: it looked as if it had been placed there with the greatest care, instead of having come to rest after a flight of at least twenty feet. The third stone fell behind me in a corner of the dining-room, and, as I sprang up and turned round, the fourth one fell on the seat of the stool on which I had been sitting. Door and windows were closed and had been for some time. The room was a small one, and there was no heavy furniture behind which even a child or a monkey could successfully hide.

My wife and baby, with the two servants, went to

her mother's house, a quarter of a mile away, and the stones went there too, and began to fall.

A retreat was made to a neighbour's house, but the stones followed again, to smash up pot plants and a table, and make a mess of the veranda generally.

In desperation I collected my small family and took them to a hotel, where only three stones fell from noon onwards.

At midday I returned to the house to find the *naneine* [the servant girl] washing baby clothes at the outdoor tap. I told her to make a cup of tea, and as she crossed the veranda to enter the house I saw a large stone rise of its own accord from the side of the steps to a height of about five feet and make straight for her. She fled into the street and was with difficulty coaxed back to complete her task.

Later, when she was laying the study table to serve the tea, a stone rose over the veranda rail and flew into the house between the partially open swing doors. It was travelling straight at my stomach, and as I stooped to catch it in its flight, it swerved some forty degrees to the right and fell on to the table, to smash glassware and a milk jug and knock to the floor a full glass jar of jelly.

At this turn in the proceedings I came to a decision – that the *naneine* must leave us, for it had been forced on my notice that the stones fell only when she was in or around the house. But when I called for her she was not to be found. She was bolting for home.

More than three hundred missiles fell in the house and on the veranda this day, including the one with a hole in it which I had already pitched into the court on two successive days; it had become an old friend!

I spent the night in the house alone, with nothing to disturb my rest, but at the usual time in the morning of the fourth day the missiles came as before, inside the house and on the veranda. Though I did not then know it – doors and windows being closed – the *naneine* was at her usual morning task in the courtyard and had been for some time.

In an hour and a half, with doors and windows still closed, fourteen stones, up to five stones in weight, an unripe melon, and a quantity of seeds fell in the dining-room and the adjoining bedroom. At nine-thirty, I gathered these up and placed them on the bed with a note for the detective officer whom I had been told to expect at ten o'clock.

I then left for my office, after thoroughly searching and locking up the house. I had to fight my way out of the outer courtyard door, round which morbidly interested people were tightly packed. The *naneine* was at the tap.

I had not been in the office more than a few minutes when I was called on the phone. Pandemonium had broken out in the house a few minutes after my departure. The police broke in and found the dining-room a mass of wreckage, caused by the fourteen stones that I had left with the note on the bed.

The communicating door had been closed and locked, but the stones had travelled horizontally from one room to another by way of a deep window recess that was common to both rooms, and in their passage had broken a window pane and a medicine bottle, and had torn down the curtains and scattered from the window-sill magazines and journals, that were now lying strewn around the dining-room floor.

Everything of a breakable nature on the table and sideboard had been smashed; also the hanging lamp and the clock.

In the bedroom the seeds were found to have entirely disappeared, and the wardrobe doors, which were perfectly fitting and had been securely locked, were found to be wide open, though nothing was missing. The green melon reposed alone on the bed.

I returned to the office just in time to receive another phone call, this time from the proprietor of the hotel, who, although I was on the most friendly terms with him, instantly demanded that I removed my family at once. There was nothing to be done but comply with his very reasonable demand, exasperating though it was. So I brought my people back to their home – hoping for the best, while fearing the worst.

A minute after leaving the hotel, and while driving through the city's main thoroughfare, a stone rose in front of the car and entered between the open leaves of the windscreen. It struck one of the party on the shoulder, without inflicting any injury, however, and came to rest on the rear seat. I picked it up. It had a hole in it, and it should have been lying in my courtyard a mile away, for I had pitched it there only a few hours before.

When we arrived in the rue Touraine, it was to find a thousand or more people filling the house, court and road outside. These were quickly dispersed without ceremony, and with them the *naneine* – and not a stone fell afterwards.

Sea-Going Ghosts

A ghost to the rescue

One day, a sailing ship plying between Liverpool and
New Brunswick, Canada, was off the coast of New-
foundland when the first mate saw a strange man
sitting in the captain's cabin and writing on a slate
used for making rough notes in preparation for entering up the ship's log. The mate reported what he had
seen to the captain, who would not at first believe
him. How could a stranger be aboard? They had been
at sea six weeks. Even a well-concealed stowaway
would have been discovered by now. Was the mate
ill? Or drunk? Or had he been day-dreaming as he
went about his routine duties? Scoff as much as he
liked, the captain could not dissuade the mate. There
had been a stranger in the captain's cabin, writing on
the slate; the mate was convinced of it.

At last the captain agreed to investigate. The cabin,
when they entered, was empty: no stranger, nothing
disturbed or out of place, no sign at all that any
unauthorized person had intruded. Except for the
slate. On it, something was written in a hand neither
the captain nor the mate recognized:

Steer to the north-west.

Every man aboard was closely questioned; each was ordered to write the words *Steer to the north-west*. But no one, from officers to captain boy, could throw any light on the puzzling event, nor did anyone's handwriting even vaguely resemble the writing on the slate.

Completely baffled, and for no other reason than superstitious curiosity, which most seamen have in abundance, the captain ordered the helmsman to steer north-west. He had no idea as he did so what he expected to find, nor how long he would be prepared to maintain such a potentially dangerous course, for it led his ship directly towards hazardous ice-floes drifting down from the Arctic.

A sharp look-out was kept and a cautious press of sail rigged. And as it turned out, the captain had not long to sustain his patience. After an hour or so of plain sailing, an iceberg was sighted dead ahead, and alongside it, a battered and broken vessel bearing a starving crew and passengers.

A rescue operation was at once organized, the shipwrecked survivors brought aboard, all of them exhausted from the effects of hunger and exposure to the elements. And it was while the first mate was helping a rescued man over the side to safety that he looked with amazement at the poor fellow's face. In every respect this was the stranger the mate had seen in the captain's cabin: no doubt about it – features, build, even dress, everything was the same as the mate vividly remembered.

At that moment the mate said nothing, but having settled the wretched man and his companions comfortably below decks and seen that their needs of hot food and drink and fresh clothes were being supplied, he went at once to the captain to report his second extraordinary story of this extraordinary day. This time the captain was more willing to listen seriously. Between them, they decided to call in the rescued captain and the stranger as soon as both men had recovered sufficiently to answer questions.

When the small party was eventually gathered later that day in the captain's cabin, the stranger – a passenger from the wrecked ship it turned out – was asked if he would be kind enough to write a few words at the captain's dictation. The reason would be made clear afterwards. The man agreed, and was asked to write *Steer to the north-west*. This done, his handwriting was compared with that on the slate, which the captain had till then kept hidden from view.

The writing penned by the stranger and the writing on the slate were identical.

The surprised man found himself replying at once to a flurry of excited questions. His answers, added to by remarks from the rescued captain and completed by details recounted by his hosts, built into an incredible solution to the story of his and his exhausted companions' rescue.

It appears that after drifting for days in their wrecked boat, the unhappy survivors had all but given up hope of reaching safety. One man only remained certain that they would be found in time. During the morning of their rescue, this man had fallen asleep so deeply that the others feared he was slipping towards death, as others had before him. But after a time, he awoke and at once told the captain with entire confidence that help was on its way and would soon reach them. During his sleep, the man said, he had dreamed he was aboard a vessel that he was sure would come to find them. He even described the ship's appearance. That ship was the very one in which they now sat, and the man was the stranger the first mate had seen.

One curious detail remained to explain: the stranger remembered nothing about the slate. He had not, in his dream, sat at the captain's table writing a message. He had wandered about, looking here and there, and could describe what he had seen. But no amount of trying produced any memory at all of the slate and the call for help written on it.

What the mate saw, if we can believe this tale, was not the ghost of a dead man, but the ghost of a living man. And if that seems too much to swallow, consider this: in the annals of psychical research there are at least sixteen well recorded cases of men and women who deliberately set out to produce their own ghosts and succeeded. One of these is quoted in a fascinating book, *Apparitions* by G. N. M. Tyrrell (Gerald Duckworth). Those who doubt the possibility that a dying man's ghost can be seen and may even perhaps write a message on a slate, a message that leads to the man's rescue so that he does not die in the end, would do well to examine what Mr Tyrrell has to say.

The Flying Dutchman

Most famous of all sea-going ghosts is *The Flying Dutchman*, the phantom ship seen by countless sailors down the years, and the inspiration of legends, poems and music.

'Tis the phantom ship, that in darkness and wrath,
Ploughs evermore the waste ocean path,
And the heart of the mariner trembles in dread,
When it crosses his vision like the ghost of the dead.

So wrote the poet, Ayres. And indeed *The Flying Dutchman* is often taken as a sign of ill omen.

There are several accounts telling how the story began. According to one Dutch legend, a certain captain had tried without success to round the notoriously dangerous Cape Horn against a head gale. But he would not give up and forced his crew to put on more and more sail, even though the gale was growing worse by the minute. All the while the reckless man drank and smoked and laughed with mad disregard for everyone's safety, including his own. Then came retribution. The Holy Ghost descended on to the vessel, no doubt with divine instructions to make the captain see sense. Instead, the crazed fellow fired off his pistol at the Third Person of the Holy Trinity, but managed only to wound his own hand, so drunken was his aim, paralysing his arm as a result.

This self-inflicted injury seems only to have added furious anger to drunken folly, for he cursed the Deity with unstinted curses and such vehemence that the Godly Apparition, its patience apparently exhausted by this crude master mariner, there and then condemned him and his luckless crew to sail *The Flying Dutchman* for ever without again putting into port and with nothing but hellish gall to drink and red-hot iron to eat and an eternal watch to keep. To this doomed captain was to be sent thereafter every worst sinner of the sea, every malicious mutineer, every coward, thief and ocean-going malcontent. Together these dregs of humanity would work an eternal passage.

Such was the evil entombed in that purgatorial boat that it spawned tempests, thick mists, and every kind of weather that seamen loathe. Thus it is that when you see the *Dutchman* scudding silently by, every sail billowed by a wind too great for a normal ship to raise a handkerchief against, you quake in your sea-boots and wonder what dreadful fate awaits you over the next high wave.

In the lore of the sea, full of superstition and courage as it is, there are many stories about phantom ships. Of them the tale told by the second mate of the

Orkney Belle, a large whaling steamer, is in many details typical:

One evening in the month of January 1911, when we were about five miles from Reykjavik, Iceland, I was standing on the bridge with the captain, a thin mist swirling over everything.

Suddenly it thinned, leaving visibility easy, when to our surprise, a sailing vessel loomed practically head on.

The captain signalled dead slow and the carpenter bawled from the deck, '*The Flying Dutchman!*'

The strange vessel slid slowly alongside, within a stone's throw, and we noticed her sails were billowing, yet there was no wind at all. She had a high poop and carved stern.

All our crew rushed to the side, but not a soul was to be seen on the strange vessel. Then three peals sounded as from a silver bell, when suddenly, this strange craft headed starboard and disappeared into the fog.

Maybe Boyles O'Reilly's poem *The Phantom Ship* passed through the second mate's head as he watched the ghostly ship, and especially this stanza:

But heaven help the ship near which the demon
    sailor steers!
The doom of those is sealed, to whom the Phantom
    Ship appears,

They'll never reach their destin'd port, they'll see
   their homes no more,
They who see *The Flying Dutchman*, never, never reach
   the shore.

The mate and crew of the *Orkney Belle*, however, some-how avoided such mysterious disaster and lived to tell their tale.

Whales with castles on their backs

One of the stories in *Further Stories from Lord Halifax's Ghost Book* tells of an old nurse who had a strange dream on two consecutive nights during the First World War. In her dream she saw what she after-wards described as 'whales with castles on their backs' circling round the third pillar of the Forth Bridge. The dream impressed the old woman so much that she wrote about it to her nephew who was at that time working on the bridge.

The letter was more important than the old nurse could know. Her nephew was busy as one of a team of men who were fortifying the pillars of the bridge against damage by submarine attack. When he read his aunt's letter he felt sure the 'whales with castles on their backs' were nothing else but submarines described by someone who had never seen a submar-ine in her life. He showed the letter to the foreman, and he too agreed that it was very curious that such a dream should be reported to them just at that time.

So the workmen were kept going day and night in order to finish protecting the pillars with concrete casings as soon as possible.

On the day after the work was completed two German submarines were spotted in the Firth of Forth, and did actually attack the bridge. Their torpedoes failed to cause any significant damage, and because the workmen had alerted the Royal Navy to the possibility of an attack, ships were standing by and one of the U-boats was captured.

Precognitive dreams – ghosts of sleep – are common. Many people experience them, and sometimes they can lead to such unusual action as this story describes. More usually, it is not till after the event dreamed about takes place in reality that the dreamer sees the importance of his night-time drama.

Wilfred Owen's ghost

Wilfred Owen was one of England's finest poets; no one has better written about the horror of war than he. And it was a tragedy of war that killed him on 4 November 1918, only a few days before the First World War came to its end. By ironic mischance his family learned of his death on the very day of the Armistice, 11 November. His brother, Harold Owen, was at that time in the Royal Navy, a lieutenant serving in the light cruiser, HMS *Astraea*, which was on station in tropical waters off Africa.

Lt Owen was very depressed, quite unable to enter into the happy mood felt by most people at the good news of the war's end. He thought he was suffering from the heat and the weakening effects of malaria. Nevertheless, he also felt something was wrong, something he could not quite identify. He was restless, uneasy, even thought of sending home a telegram asking whether his brothers Wilfred and Colin were well. But he decided against doing anything; the feeling was too vague.

It was in this 'mood' that Harold Owen saw his brother Wilfred's ghost some time *before* news of Wilfred's death reached him. The experience is described in the third volume, *War*, of Harold Owen's biography, *Journey from Obscurity*:

I had gone down to my cabin thinking to write some letters. I drew aside the door curtain and stepped inside and to my amazement I saw Wilfred sitting in my chair. I felt shock running through me with appalling force and with it I could feel the blood draining away from my face. I did not rush towards him but walked jerkily into the cabin – all my limbs stiff and slow to respond. I did not sit down but looking at him I spoke quietly: 'Wilfred, how did you get here?' He did not rise and I saw that he was involuntarily immobile, but his eyes which had never left mine were alive with the familiar look of trying to make me understand; when I spoke his whole face broke into his sweetest and most endearing dark smile. I felt no fear – I had not when I first drew my door curtain and saw him there; only exquisite mental pleasure at thus beholding him. All I was conscious of was a sensation of enormous shock and profound astonishment that he should be there in my cabin. I spoke again: 'Wilfred, dear, how can you be here, it's just not possible . . . ' But still he did not speak but only smiled his most gentle smile. This not speaking did not now as it had done at first seem strange or even unnatural; it was not only in some inexplicable way perfectly natural but radiated a quality which made his presence with me undeniably right and in no way out of the ordinary. I loved having him there: I could not, and did not want to try to, understand how he had got there. I was content to accept him; that he was here with me was sufficient. I could not question anything, the meeting in itself was complete and strangely perfect. He was in uniform and I remember thinking how out of place the khaki looked amongst the cabin furnishings. With this thought I must have turned my eyes from him; when I looked back my cabin chair was empty . . .

I felt the blood run slowly back to my face and looseness into my limbs and with these an overpowering sense of emptiness and absolute loss . . . I wondered if I had been dreaming, but looking down I saw that I was still standing. Suddenly I felt terribly tired, and moving to my bunk I lay down; instantly I went into a deep oblivious sleep. When I woke up I knew with absolute certainty that Wilfred was dead.

Harold Owen's story is one among many of a similar kind recorded by hundreds of people over many years. Whether he actually saw the returned spirit of his brother or whether the apparition was some kind of telepathic communication from his distressed family, or indeed whether it was none of these but simply a vivid waking dream brought on by the tropical heat and Mr Owen's uneasy feelings and wonderings about his brothers, everyone must decide for themselves. There is no proving any of these possibilities. What we can be sure about is that, though the legend of *The Flying Dutchman* might well be nothing more than a seaman's yarn, Harold Owen, the old nurse, and the first mate and crew of the *Orkney Belle* all experienced something no one dare dismiss. The difficult thing is to discover how to interpret what they experienced, to find out how those experiences happened, and why, and what they mean.

The Mystery Ghost
of Amherst, Nova Scotia

When the trouble began, Amherst, now a county town, was no more than a large village, neat and trim and quiet. But in the summer of 1878 its rural peace was disturbed by a strange drama which, before it was played out over a year later, had become world famous. To this day the Amherst haunting remains Canada's most puzzling ghost story.

The time, then, is high summer 1878; the place, a two-storeyed house on the corner of Princess Street and Church Street, a tidy building, painted yellow and with bright red geraniums blooming in the ground-floor windows. Here lived a collection of people who, like actors in a play, each had a part in the real-life drama about to begin:

Daniel Teed, thirty-five years old, head of the house and foreman at the Amherst Shoe Factory – a respected, hard-working and well-liked citizen.

Olive, Daniel's wife, a sober, good-living woman.

Willie, aged five, a strong, healthy lad with blue eyes and curly brown hair. His favourite pastime, it seems, was taunting the hens that pecked about at the back of the house.

George, seventeen months old, an intelligent baby and the village as well as the family favourite.

Two 'boarders': John Teed, Daniel's younger brother and a farm worker; and William Cox, Olive's brother and a shoemaker employed at Daniel's factory.

Under Daniel's care and protection lived two of his wife's sisters. They joined the household after the death of their mother and the remarriage of their father. They were Jennie (or Jane) Cox, aged twenty-two, the village beauty and therefore much admired and courted by the local young men; and Esther Cox, aged nineteen, the central figure in the drama.

Unlike her sister Jennie, Esther seems to have been very ordinary to look at: short in stature, plump, with a pale complexion and unremarkable features, except for large blue-grey eyes that stared at you sometimes in an unsettling way. The village children liked her, and when she was in good spirits she could be kind and gentle. But when she was thwarted or out of sorts she sulked and was ill-tempered. Always she had a strong independent will and preferred having her own way.

A few days before the haunting began, Esther had had some unpleasant experiences. On 27 August, Daniel complained that for ten nights past his cow, which was kept behind the house, had been secretly milked, thus reducing the yield available for the family next day. Who could be the thief? Everyone knew that

Esther loved milk and, naturally, suspicion fell on her. But there was no proof, so nothing was done.

That night, Esther had a vivid and terrifying dream, which she told Olive about next morning. In her dream she had been attacked by hundreds of huge black bulls with blood dripping from their mouths and feet made of fire. She was so distressed by the dream that she wanted Olive to go with her to a fortune-teller to ask what the dream meant. Olive, a good Methodist like all the family, would not hear of such a thing.

On the evening of 28 August the most distressing experience of all occurred. After supper, Esther's boy-friend, Bob McNeal, called and took her for a ride in a two-seated open buggy. It was a thundery night and rain soon began to fall. Well after dark, at about ten o'clock, Esther arrived home in a hysterical state, dishevelled and soaked to the skin. She would explain nothing of what had happened until a whole month later. She then claimed that Bob had taken her to a lonely spot and attacked her. She had been saved by the chance approach of another carriage, at the sound of which Bob drove off, at a dangerous pace, back to the village, where he dumped his girlfriend and dashed away, leaving the village there and then and never, as it turned out, returning again.

Was Esther's story true? Did Bob leave Amherst out of shame for his actions and fear of the consequences? Or did something else happen about which

Esther did not want to talk? We do not know. What we do know is that for days after the event she was speechless and red-eyed from weeping.

Exactly a week after Bob's alleged attack, the haunting began. A foggy wet night sent everyone early to bed. Jennie, who shared Esther's bed, was nearly asleep when Esther asked if it was not the 4 September. Jennie agreed that it was and told Esther to go to sleep. From that moment the trouble started.

The only detailed record of the extraordinary story was written by a Mr Walter Hubbell in a book called *The Haunted House* first published in 1879. Hubbell met all the family, even staying with them during the last few months of the disturbances. Unfortunately, he was not a very scientific investigator; in fact he was a music-hall conjurer with an eye for a money-making entertainment. His sensational book sold thousands of copies and made him famous. We know, however, that his account is carefully written so that the exciting moments are made as dramatic as can be, and that some of the things said by Esther and the others sound 'stagey' and unreal – made-up, in fact. Nevertheless, his record is fascinating; readers must simply decide for themselves which parts are likely to be true and which are not. This said, let Mr Hubbell continue the story in his own fashion, joining him at the moment when Esther is lying in the dark, brooding on her misery.

*

The room in which the girls were in bed together was in the front of the house, in the second storey, at the head of the stairs, and next to the room occupied by Mr and Mrs Teed and their children, and had one window directly over the front door. They had lain perfectly quiet for about ten minutes, when Esther jumped out of bed with a scream, exclaiming that there was a mouse under the bedclothes. Her scream startled her sister, who was almost asleep, and she also got out of bed and at once lighted the lamp. They then both searched the bed, but could not find the mouse. Supposing it to be inside the mattress, Jennie remarked that they were both fools to be afraid of a little harmless mouse.

'For see,' said she, 'it is inside the mattress; look how the straw is being moved about by it. The mouse has gotten inside somehow and cannot get out because it is lost. Let us get back to bed, Esther; it cannot harm us now.'

So they put out the light and got into bed again. After listening for a few minutes without hearing the straw move in the mattress the girls fell asleep.

On the following night the girls heard something moving under their bed, and Esther exclaimed, 'There is that mouse again; let us get up and kill it. I am not going to be worried by a mouse every night.'

They arose, and one of them lighted the lamp. On hearing a rustling in a green pasteboard box filled with patchwork, which was under the bed, they placed

the box in the middle of the room, and were amazed
to see it spring up a foot into the air, and then fall to
the floor and turn over on its side. The girls could not
believe their own eyes, so Jennie again placed the box
in the middle of the room and both watched it
intently, when the same thing was repeated. Both
Jennie and Esther were now thoroughly frightened,
and screamed as loudly as they could for Daniel, who
quickly put on some clothing and came into their
room to ascertain what was the matter. They
described what had occurred, but he only laughed,
and after pushing the box under the bed, remarked
that they must be crazy, or perhaps had been dreaming; and after grumbling because his rest had been
disturbed, he went back to bed. The next morning
the girls both declared that the box had really moved
upward into the air, and had fallen to the floor, and
rolled over on its side, where Daniel had found it on
entering their room; but as no one believed them,
they concluded it was no use to talk of the singular
occurrence.

After breakfast, Jennie went to Mr Dunlop's to
work (she was a tailoress), and the rest of the household set about their usual daily business, leaving Mrs
Teed, Esther and the boys alone in the house. After
dinner, Mrs Teed sat in the parlour, sewing, while
Esther went out for a walk. The afternoon was delight-
fully cool, a pleasant breeze blowing from the bay.
Walking is very pleasant when there is no dust, but

Amherst is such a dusty village, especially when the wind blows from the bay and so scatters the dust of the unpaved streets, that it is impossible to walk on any of them with comfort; and Esther, finding this to be the case, retraced her steps homeward, stopping at the post office and at Bird's book store, where she bought a bottle of ink from Miss Blanche and then returned home. After supper, Esther took her accustomed seat on the doorstep, remaining there until the moon had risen. It was a beautiful moonlit night, almost as bright as day; and while seated there looking at the moon, she remarked to Jennie that she would surely have good luck during the month because she had seen the new moon over her shoulder.

At half-past eight o'clock in the evening, Esther complained of feeling feverish, and was advised by Mrs Teed and Jennie to go to bed, which she did. At about ten o'clock Jennie also retired. After she had been in bed with Esther some fifteen minutes, the latter jumped with a sudden bound into the centre of the room, taking all the bedclothes with her, exclaiming:

'My God! What is the matter with me? I'm dying!'

Jennie at once got out of bed, thinking her sister had an attack of nightmare; but, when she had lighted the lamp, was much alarmed at Esther's appearance as she stood in the centre of the room with her short hair almost standing on end, her face blood-red and her eyes looking as if they would start from their sockets, while her hands were grasping the back of a chair so tightly that her fingernails sank into the soft wood. And, truly, she was an object to be looked on with astonishment, as she stood there in her white nightgown, trembling with fear. Jennie called as loudly as she could for assistance; for she, too, was thoroughly frightened by this time, and did not know what to do. Mrs Teed was the first to enter the room, having first thrown a shawl round her shoulders, for it was a very chilly night; Daniel dressed hurriedly, as did William Cox and John Teed, and the three men entered the room at almost the same instant.

'Why, what in thunder ails you, Esther?' asked Daniel, while William Cox and John Teed exclaimed in the same breath, 'She's mad!'

Mrs Teed was speechless with amazement; and they all stood looking at the girl, not knowing what to do to relieve her terrible agony. Suddenly, she became pale and seemed to be growing very weak, and in a short time became so weak that she had to be assisted to the bed. After sitting on the edge of the bed for a moment, and gazing about the room with a vacant stare, she started to her feet with a wild yell and said that she felt as if she was about to burst in pieces.

'Great Heavens!' exclaimed Mrs Teed. 'What shall we do with her? She's crazy!'

Jennie, who generally retained her presence of mind, said in a soothing tone, 'Come, Esther, get into bed again.'

As she could not do so without assistance, her sister helped her in, when she gasped in a choking voice, 'I am swelling up and shall certainly burst, I know I shall.'

Daniel looked at her, and remarked in a startled tone, 'Why, the girl is swelling! Olive, just look at her; even her hands are swollen. Lay your hand on her; she is as hot as fire.'

While the family stood looking at her and wondering what to do to relieve her, for her entire body had now swollen and she was screaming in pain and grinding her teeth as if in a fit, a loud report, like one peal of thunder without that terrible rumbling afterwards, was heard in the room. They all, except Esther, who was in bed, started instantly to their feet and stood motionless, literally paralysed with surprise.

Mrs Teed was the first to speak, exclaiming, 'My God! The house has been struck by a thunderbolt, and I know my boys have been killed!' She rushed from the room, followed by her husband, William Cox and John Teed; Jennie remained by Esther's bedside.

On finding the children both sleeping soundly they returned to the room and stood looking at Esther in silence, wondering what had produced the terrible sound. Going to the window, Mrs Teed raised the curtain and saw the stars shining brightly and all were then satisfied it had not been thunder they had heard. Just as she let the curtain down again, three terrific reports were heard in the room, apparently coming from under the bed on which Esther lay. These reports were so loud that the whole room shook, and Esther, who a moment before had been fearfully swollen, and in such great pain, immediately assumed her natural appearance and sank into a state of calm repose. As soon as they were sure that it was sleep, not death, that had taken possession of her, they all left the room, except Jennie, who went again to bed beside her sister, but could not sleep for the balance of the night, through nervous excitement.

The next day, Esther remained in bed until about nine o'clock, when she arose, apparently herself again, and got her own breakfast . . . At supper that evening the usual conversation occurred about the unearthly sounds, but as not one of them could offer explanation they concluded it was too deep a matter for them to talk about, and all agreed to keep it secret and not inform any of their friends or neighbours what had transpired. They knew that no one would believe that such strange, unknown sounds had been heard under the bed, nor that Esther had been so singularly affected from unknown causes. About four nights after the loud reports had been heard, Esther had a similar attack. It came on at ten o'clock at night, just as she was about to get into bed. This time, however, she managed to get into the bed before the attack had swelled her to any great extent.

Jennie Cox, who had already retired, advised her

to remain perfectly quiet, consoling her with the hope that if she did so the attack would in all probability pass away, and she would then be able to go to sleep without further inconvenience. Esther remained perfectly motionless as advised, but had only been so for about five minutes when, to the consternation of both, all the bedclothes, except the bottom sheet on which they lay, flew off and settled down in a confused heap in a far corner of the room. They could see them passing through the air by the light of the kerosene lamp, which had been lit and was standing on the table; both screamed and then Jennie fainted. And was it not enough to have frightened any woman and made her faint?

On hearing the screams, the entire family rushed into the room; there lay all the bedclothes in the corner; Esther fearfully swollen, but entirely conscious, and Jennie lying as if she were dead. Indeed she looked like a corpse as the light of the lamp, which Daniel held in his hand, fell upon her pale face.

Mrs Teed was the first to recover her senses and, seeing that the forms of her two sisters were exposed, quickly took up the bedclothes and placed them on the girls again. She had no sooner done so than they instantly flew off to the same corner of the room, and the pillow, from under Esther's head, came flying through the air and struck John Teed in the face. This was too much for John's nerves, and he immediately left the room, after remarking that 'he had had enough of it', and could not be induced to return to sit on the edges of the bed with the others who, in that way, managed to keep the bedclothes in place over the girls. Jennie had by this time recovered from her fainting spell, and William Cox went down to the kitchen for a bucket of water to bathe Esther's head, which was aching, when, just as he got to the door of the room again with the bucket of water, a succession of reports was heard that seemed to come from the bed whence the two girls lay. These reports were so loud that the whole room trembled from their vibrations; and Esther, who a moment before had been swollen, assumed her natural appearance, and in a few minutes fell into an apparently healthful sleep. As all seemed right again the entire family retired, but could sleep no more that night.

The next morning Jennie and Esther were both very weak, particularly Esther. She arose, however, when her sister did and lay down on the sofa in the parlour. At breakfast the members of the family all agreed that a doctor had better be sent for, so in the afternoon Daniel left the factory early and went to see Dr Carritte, who laughed heartily when Daniel told him what had occurred, and said he would call in the evening, and remain until the following morning, if necessary; but did not hesitate to say that what Daniel told him was all nonsense, remarking that he knew no such tomfoolery would occur while he was in the house.

As the hands of the clock pointed to ten that evening, in walked the doctor. Wishing everybody a hearty good evening, he took a seat near Esther, who had been in bed since nine o'clock, but as yet had not been afflicted with one of her strange attacks of swelling, nor had any of the strange noises been heard. The doctor felt her pulse, looked at her tongue, and then told the family that she seemed to be suffering from nervous excitement, and had evidently received a tremendous shock of some kind. Just after he had given this opinion, and while he was still sitting by her side, the pillow on which her head was lying came out from under her head, with the exception of one corner, as if it was pulled by some invisible power, and straightening itself out, as if filled with air, remained so a moment, and then went back to its place again, under her head.

The doctor's large blue eyes opened to their utmost capacity as he asked in a low tone, 'Did you see that? It went back again.'

'So it did,' remarked John Teed, 'but if it moves again, it will not go back, for I intend to hold on to it, even if it did bang me over the head last night.'

John had no sooner spoken these words than out came the pillow from under Esther's head as before. He waited until it had just started back again, then grasped it with both his hands and held it with all his strength, and he was, it must be remembered, a strong, healthy young farmer. However, all his efforts to hold it were unavailing, as it was pulled away from him by some invisible power stronger than himself, and again assumed its position under the young girl's head. Just imagine his astonishment! All the members of the family told me that they never saw anyone so completely dumbfounded as John Teed was at that moment.

'How wonderful!' exclaimed Dr Carritte.

The doctor arose from his chair; and the loud reports commenced under the bed as on the previous nights. He looked beneath the bed but failed to ascertain what had caused the sounds. He walked to the door and the sounds followed him, being now produced on the floor of the room. In about a minute after this the bedclothes flew off again; and before they had been put back on the bed to cover Esther, the distinct sound as of some person writing on the wall with a metallic instrument was heard. All looked at the wall whence the sound of writing came, when, to their great astonishment, there could be plainly read these words:

Esther Cox, you are mine to kill

Every person in the room could see the writing plainly, and yet a moment before nothing was to be seen but the plain wall. I have seen this writing; it was deeply indented in the wall and looked to me as if it had been written with a dull instrument, probably a large iron spike. I say a dull instrument because the writing had a very uneven appearance, and the invisible power that wrote it was certainly neither an elegant nor an accomplished penman . . .

The reader can probably imagine their utter amazement at what had just taken place. There they stood around the bed of this suffering girl, each watching the other, to see that there could be no possible mistake about what they saw and heard. They all knew that marvellous things had taken place, for each had heard and seen them with his or her own eyes and ears. Still, they dare not trust their own senses; it was all so strange, so different from any previous experience they had ever had, or heard of others having had, that they were all, without a single exception, awed into fearful silence. The terrible words written on the wall – *Esther Cox, you are mine to kill.* What could their import be? Were they true? What had written them? All that was known was that they had heard the writing, and had seen the letters appear, one by one upon the wall, but there their knowledge stopped, and everything to their understanding was as blank as the wall had been before the invisible power, that threatened to commit murder, had exposed upon that smooth white surface the terrifying sentence in characters nearly a foot in height.

As Dr Carritte stood in the door wondering what it all meant, a large piece of plaster came flying from the wall of the room, turning a corner in its flight, and fell at his feet. The good doctor picked it up mechanically, and placed it on a chair; he was too astonished to speak. Just after he had placed the plaster on the chair, the fearfully loud pounding sounds commenced again with redoubled power, this time shaking the entire room and all it contained, including the doctor and other persons. All this time, Esther lay upon the bed almost frightened to death. After this stage of things had continued for about two hours all became quiet, and Esther, poor girl, went to sleep. The doctor decided not to give her any medicine until the next morning, when he said he would call and give her something to quiet her nerves.

As to the sounds, and movements of the bedclothes and plaster and the mysterious writing, he could say nothing. He had heard and seen, and could not doubt his own senses; but had no theory to offer that would solve the unanswerable facts he had witnessed in the manifestations of some invisible power seeming to possess human intelligence of a very low and most demoniac type.

The next morning Dr Carritte called, as he had promised, and was greatly surprised to see Esther up and dressed, helping Mrs Teed to wash the breakfast dishes. She told him she felt all right again, except that she was so nervous that any sudden sound startled her and made her jump. Having occasion to go down into the cellar with a pan of milk she came running up, out of breath, and stated there was someone in the cellar who had thrown a piece of plank at her. The doctor went down to see for himself, Esther remaining in the dining-room. The cellar stairs being directly under the stairway in the hall, the door to the cellar opened into the dining-room. In a moment he came up again, remarking that there was not any person down there to throw a piece of plank or anything else.

'Esther, come down with me,' said he.

They both went down; when to their great surprise, several potatoes came flying at their heads; and both ran up the cellar stairs. The doctor immediately left the house, and called again in the evening with several very powerful sedatives, morphia being one, which he administered to Esther at about ten o'clock, as she lay in bed. She still complained of her nervousness, and said she felt as though electricity was passing all through her body. He had given her the sedative medicine, and had just stated that she would have a good night's rest, when the sounds commenced, only they were very much louder and in more rapid succession than on the previous nights. Presently the sounds left the room and were heard distinctly on the roof of the house. The doctor instantly left the house and went into the street, where he heard the sounds in the open air.

On returning to the house he was more nonplussed than ever; and informed the family that when in the street it seemed as if some person was on the roof with a heavy sledgehammer, pounding away to try and break through the shingles. Being a moonlit night he could see distinctly that there was not any person upon the roof. He remained on this occasion until midnight, when all became quiet and he departed, promising to call the next day. When he had gotten as far as the front gate, the heavy poundings commenced again on the roof with great violence, and continued until he had gone about two hundred yards from the cottage, at which distance he could still hear them distinctly. Dr Carritte told me this himself. The next week it became known throughout Amherst that strange manifestations of an unknown power, that was invisible, were going on at Daniel Teed's cottage. The mysterious sounds had been heard by people in the street as they passed the house, and several accounts had been printed in the *Amherst Gazette* and copied in other papers. The pounding sounds now commenced in the morning and were to be heard all day. Poor Esther, whom the power had chosen as its victim, always felt relieved when the sounds were produced.

About one month after the commencement of the wonders, the Reverend Dr Edwin Clay, the well-known Baptist clergyman, called at the house to see and hear the wonders of which he had read some accounts in the newspapers, but was desirous of seeing and hearing for himself; and he was fortunate enough to have his desire fully gratified by hearing the loudest kind of sound, and seeing the writing on the wall. When he left the house he was fully satisfied that Esther did not in any way produce the sounds herself, and that the family had nothing whatever to do with them. He, however, agreed with Dr Carritte in his theory that her nerves had received a shock of some kind, making her, in some mysterious manner, an electric battery, his idea being that invisible flashes of lightning left her person and that the sounds, which every person could hear so distinctly, were simply minute peals of thunder. So convinced was he that he had ascertained the cause and that there was no deception in regard to the manifestations of the power, that he delivered lectures on the subject and drew large audiences. He always nobly defended Esther Cox and the family, when charged by unthinking people with fraud, and spoke of the affair often from the pulpit. The Reverend R. A. Temple, the well-known Wesleyan minister, pastor of the Wesleyan Church in Amherst, which the Teed family attended, also witnessed the manifestations. He saw, among other strange things, a bucket of cold water become agitated and, to all appearances, boil while standing on the kitchen table.

At this point in the haunting, Esther and her home became notorious. People flocked from everywhere to see for themselves the exhibition of ghostly activity. The police had to keep order, so big were the crowds day after day. Finally, such unaccustomed fame made Esther ill, and she was confined to bed for two weeks, during which time the disturbances ceased. She was then sent to a married sister at Sackville, New Brunswick, to recuperate for another two weeks, and again was unmolested.

So far there is little doubt that the haunting – clearly a poltergeist case – was genuine. But when Esther returned home, a fresh outbreak of activity produced some suspicious effects, and many experts believe that Esther herself was deliberately responsible for these frauds, probably in order to keep herself in the limelight. She was, after all, not very attractive and always overshadowed by her beautiful sister. She had undoubtedly received some kind of shock, as Dr Carritte realized, when out with Bob McNeal. So Esther was in low spirits and looking perhaps for attention and success. The haunting brought her both, and it was quite natural, even if wrong, for her to try and keep that attention and success for herself as long as possible. Other young people who have been the victims of poltergeists have been tempted in the same way and have ended up perpetrating ridiculous frauds on a gullible public. Esther may even have been aided and abetted by Mr Hubbell himself; he certainly put her on public exhibition on one occasion and asked the 'audience' to pay money to see Esther produce her ghostly effects!

Let's continue with Mr Hubbell's account from the point where Esther returns from her sister's, and decide for ourselves whether the happenings after he illness seem as genuine and believable as all that happened before it.

*

On returning to Daniel's cottage, the most startling and peculiar features of the power took place. One night while in bed with her sister Jennie, in another room, their room having been changed in the hope that the power would not follow them, she told Jennie that she could hear a voice informing her that the house was to be set on fire that night by a ghost. The voice stated it had once lived on the earth, but had been dead for some years and was now only a ghost.

The members of the household were at once called in and told what Esther had said. They all laughed and informed the girls that no such thing as that could possibly have been said, because there were no ghosts. The Reverend Dr Clay had stated that all the trouble had been caused by electricity.

'And', said Daniel, 'electricity cannot set the house on fire, unless it comes from a cloud in the form of lightning.'

To the amazement and consternation of all present, while they were talking and laughing about the ridiculous statement the girls had made, as having come from the voice of a ghost to Esther, all saw a lighted match fall from the ceiling to the bed, having come out of the air, which would certainly have set the bedclothing on fire, had not Jennie put it out instantly. During the next ten minutes, eight or ten lighted matches fell on the bed and about the room, out of the air, but were all extinguished before anything could be set on fire by them. In the course of the night the loud sounds commenced again.

It seems that about three weeks after Dr Carritte's first visit to the cottage, Jennie stated that she believed that the power that made the sounds and lit the matches could hear and understand all that was said and perhaps could see them. The moment she had finished the sentence, three distinct reports were heard; and, on Daniel requesting Dr Carritte to ask the power if it could hear, three reports were heard, which shook the entire house. Dr Carritte remarked at the time that it was very singular. Daniel then asked if the power could tell how many persons were in the room, and not receiving a reply, repeated the question in this form, 'How many persons are in the room? Give a knock on the floor for each one.'

Six distinct knocks were instantly made by the power; and there were just six persons in the room at the time, they being Dr Carritte, Daniel Teed, his wife, Esther, Jennie and William Cox; John Teed having left the room after poor Esther had buried her face in the pillow as she lay in bed, trembling with fright.

The family could now converse with the power in this way. It would knock once for a negative answer, and three times for an answer in the affirmative, giving only two knocks when in doubt about a reply.

This system of communication had been suggested by a visitor. And it was in this way that they carried on a conversation the night the matches fell upon the bed from the ceiling.

Daniel asked if the house would really be set on fire, and the reply was 'Yes'. And a fire was started in about five minutes in the following manner. The invisible ghost that had spoken to Esther took a dress belonging to her that was hanging on a nail in the wall near the door and, after rolling it up and placing it under the bed before their eyes, but so quickly that they could not prevent the action, set it on fire. Fortunately the dress was at once pulled from under the bed by Daniel, and the fire extinguished before any serious damage had been done to the material.

Daniel told me that when the dress was being rolled up and put under the bed, they could not see the ghost doing it. All was then quiet for the rest of the night; no one daring to go to bed, however, for fear another fire would be kindled.

The next morning all was consternation in the cottage. Daniel and his wife were afraid that the ghost would start a fire in some inaccessible place, where it could not be extinguished, in which case no one could save the cottage from burning to the ground.

All members of the family were now fully convinced that the mysterious power was really what it claimed to be, a ghost of some very evil man who had once lived upon the earth, and in some unknown manner managed to torture poor Esther, as only such a ghost would . . .

About three days after the ghost had tried to set

the bed on fire by lighting it with the burning dress, Mrs Teed, while churning in the kitchen, noticed smoke issuing from the cellar door, which, as I have already explained, opened into the dining-room. Esther at the time was seated in the dining-room, and had been there an hour or more, previous to which she had been in the kitchen assisting her sister to wash the breakfast dishes. Mrs Teed was the first to recover from the shock, and seizing a bucket of drinking water, always kept standing on the kitchen table, she rushed down the cellar stairs, and in the far corner of the cellar saw a band of shavings blazing up almost to the joists of the main floor of the house. In the meantime, Esther had reached the cellar and stood as if petrified with astonishment. Mrs Teed poured what water the bucket contained (for in the excitement she had spilled more than half on her way down) into the burning shavings, and both she and Esther, being almost choked with smoke, ran up the cellar stairs, and out of the house into Princess Street, crying 'Fire! Fire!' as loudly as they could.

Their cries aroused the entire neighbourhood. Several men rushed in, and while some smothered the flames with rugs from the dining-room floor, others put them out entirely with water obtained from a large butt into which the rainwater ran.

From this point on, the effects increased in number and oddity. Chairs and other furniture danced about the house, Esther was said to come downstairs 'seeming to fly', a curry comb followed her about, pulled along, some said, by a black string held by Esther! Of course, instances of trickery do not disprove all the phenomena and if only Esther Cox had been properly examined by qualified people and her affliction carefully recorded in a scientific manner we might today understand more about poltergeists than we do. Certainly, whatever silliness she resorted to towards the end of the affair, her story remains one of the most interesting and baffling of all such experiences.

A School Haunting

Several young readers have written to me about the ghosts that are supposed to haunt their schools. A girl from Worcester told me about her school's first headmistress who was born and died in the building, and whose spectre is said to walk the classrooms at night (though how anyone has found that out it would be interesting to know). Likewise, I'm told that Sarah Siddons, the great actress, haunts the school named after her at Paddington Green, and that another London school, Marylebone Central, which is built on the site of an old graveyard, has ghostly visitors in, of all places, the girls' showers. At another school the clocktower is said to have been locked up after a prefect had an unpleasant experience there. She was working at a table in the tower one day. Nearby lay a pair of scissors. Suddenly the scissors rose up into the air and passed right through the startled girl – or so the story goes!

The trouble with most accounts of this kind is that there is so little sound evidence to support them. As everyone knows, schoolboys and girls take great pleasure in scaring one another with spinechilling, but entirely invented, tales of horror and suspense. Whether the stories I've mentioned are true or not I cannot say, but one schoolboy ghost story which was carefully examined by various people at the time it happened is persuasive and certainly interesting. It took place many years ago now and concerns the apparition of a boy called John Daniel.

John had been dead more than seven weeks when his ghost was seen by some of his old schoolmates. At that time, in 1728, Beaminster School, Dorset, was held, as many schools were in those days, in a gallery of the local parish church. There was an entrance to the schoolroom leading directly from the churchyard, and every Saturday after class the key to the door was delivered to one of the parish officers by one or other of the children. On Saturday 22 June 1728, the teacher dismissed his pupils as usual. Twelve of the boys then stayed in the churchyard to play football. It was just about midday. After a while four of the boys went back inside the schoolroom to look for pens they had left behind. As they searched, they were startled by a noise in the church, a noise they later described as being like that made by striking a brass pan.

They ran back to their friends and told them what they had heard. Together they decided that someone was hiding in order to try and frighten them. So all twelve went back into the school gallery to hunt for the culprit. But they could find no one.

As they were walking back down the stairs they heard another noise, this time in the gallery itself. Terrified now, they ran into the churchyard and round the church to the west door. There they stood listening. To their surprise they heard what sounded like someone preaching a sermon. After a short time the preaching was succeeded by the sound of a congregation singing hymns, which also continued for a while before fading away.

All this seemed quite inexplicable, and as nothing else unusual was heard once the singing ended, the boys returned to their game.

A little while later, one of the boys went into the schoolroom to pick up some belongings. He was stopped in his tracks as he entered the room by the sight of a coffin lying on one of the benches not six feet from him. Not surprisingly, the lad turned tail and fled to the safety of his friends, to whom he gabbled out this new turn in events. The boys thronged to the school door and looked inside. Five of them had a clear view into the schoolroom and each saw not only the coffin but the figure of John Daniel sitting near it but further into the room. The other seven boys, their view partly blocked by the five in front of them, saw only the coffin.

Now John Daniel, as I said earlier, had been dead seven weeks and all but one of the boys who saw his ghost had been to school with him. Amongst them was John's half-brother, and he, seeing the apparition,

cried out, 'There sits our John, with just such a coat on as I have, with a pen in his hand, and a book before him and a coffin by him. I'll throw a stone at him.'

The other boys tried to stop him, but he would not listen, saying, as he threw a pebble at the ghost, 'Take that!'

The ghost vanished immediately.

It is easy to imagine the excitement the boys now felt. All twelve had heard the eerie noises and had seen the spectral coffin and the unbelievable appearance of a dead friend's ghost. Naturally, they wanted to tell people their story, and soon the whole of Beaminster knew about the goings-on in the schoolroom. No doubt some people dismissed the news as the fanciful imaginings of a few summer-hot children; but there were others, important members of the community, who took the boys seriously. Each was carefully cross-examined by Colonel Broadrep, a local magistrate, and he found that each lad's story agreed closely with the others', even to the detail of the hinges on the coffin lid. The coffin itself was, to judge by the boys' descriptions, exactly like the one in which John Daniel had been buried.

Of course, the boys might have cooked up the entire tale between them. They had known John well, after all, had no doubt attended his funeral, and therefore had seen the coffin as it was borne slowly to its grave. On the other hand, for twelve boys aged between nine

and thirteen to stick by a deliberate lie and to make
not one slip either in the major details or in their own
versions of what happened, even under the kind of
repetitive questioning they were subjected to, required
rather more tenacity and self-confidence than any
twelve boys can ordinarily muster. One or two
together might have pulled it off. But twelve questioned separately by a man like the good Colonel –
never!

Besides, there was also the fact that one of the
twelve had never seen John Daniel. This young witness had come to the village after John's death. He
was twelve years old and was one of the five who saw
John's apparition. He had no memory of the real,
living John Daniel to go on. To sustain a lie as detailed
as the story told by him and his new schoolfriends he
would have to learn a great many facts from the boys
who had known John *and be able to repeat them as though
he had seen these things at first hand* in reply to questions
asked him on his own by the Colonel, questions the
boys could not anticipate and so could not specially
prepare answers for. Yet during his examination by
Colonel Broadrep, this boy, a quiet, gentle fellow by
all accounts, gave an exact description of John Daniel,
and mentioned one vital clue not noticed by any of
the other boys. One of John's hands, he said, had a
white cloth bound round it. When the woman who
had prepared the dead John's body for burial was
questioned later, she swore on oath that she had

removed a white bandage from one of the boy's hands, a fact no one else had mentioned till this time.

We cannot now discover whether the boys saw a ghost or were lying. It seems, however, that Colonel Broadrep believed their story, for as a result of his report John Daniel's body was exhumed in order that an inquest could be held on it. John had been found dead about two hundred yards from his home, and had been buried without investigation because his mother swore that the boy was subject to fits. Everyone therefore assumed that John had had a fit and had died from it. The inquest now discovered that his death had not been so straightforward. John had, in fact, been strangled. Someone had murdered him.

Aidan Chambers
Haunted Houses £2.99

Out of the darkness they creep, filling empty hallways with echoes of deathly footsteps, mournful howling and shrieks of terror . . .

Enter these haunted houses and discover their horrifying hidden secrets. Here are ten chilling true stories to take you deep inside the places where people have seen ghosts, heard them and, most frightening of all, *felt* them.

This Place is Haunted £2.50

Haunted houses, gruesome groans, the moans of tortured spirits that lurk in forgotten cellars; eerie shuffling and mysterious sounds in the night . . .

Get ready to meet your nightmares in these terrifying true stories of haunted places, and you'll soon be longing for the morning light.

All Pan books are available at your local bookshop or newsagent, or can be ordered direct from the publisher. Indicate the number of copies required and fill in the form below.

Send to: **CS Department, Pan Books Ltd., P.O. Box 40, Basingstoke, Hants. RG21 2YT.**

or phone: 0256 469551 (Ansaphone), quoting title, author and Credit Card number.

Please enclose a remittance* to the value of the cover price plus: 60p for the first book plus 30p per copy for each additional book ordered to a maximum charge of £2.40 to cover postage and packing.

*Payment may be made in sterling by UK personal cheque, postal order, sterling draft or international money order, made payable to Pan Books Ltd. -

Alternatively by Barclaycard/Access:

Card No.

Signature:

Applicable only in the UK and Republic of Ireland.

While every effort is made to keep prices low, it is sometimes necessary to increase prices at short notice. Pan Books reserve the right to show on covers and charge new retail prices which may differ from those advertised in the text or elsewhere.

NAME AND ADDRESS IN BLOCK LETTERS PLEASE:

....

Name———————————————————————————

Address———————————————————————————

————————————————————————————————

————————————————————————————————

————————————————————————————————

3/87